ORBITS

SENIOR AUTHORS
Virginia A. Arnold
Carl B. Smith

LITERATURE CONSULTANTS
Joan I. Glazer
Margaret H. Lippert

READING EXPRESS
MACMILLAN

Macmillan Publishing Company
New York

Collier Macmillan Publishers
London

Macmillan Publishing Company
866 Third Avenue
New York, N.Y. 10022
Collier Macmillan Canada, Inc.

Printed in the United States of America

ISBN 0-02-160090-2

9 8 7

ACKNOWLEDGEMENTS

The publisher gratefully acknowledges permission to reprint the following copyrighted material:

Cover Design: Bass and Goldman Associates

Illustration Credits: Andrea Baruffi, 87–93, 133–139, 205–211, 213; Patti Boyd, 230–231; Randy Chewing, 190–203; Bradley Clark, 149–157; Pat Cummings, 142–145, 147; Dee de Rosa, 171–179; Susan Dodge, 32–33; Mary Duarte, 217–224; Len Ebert, 43–51; Allan Eitzen, 94–95; Peggy Fortnum, 232–242; Marla Frazee, 10–11, 12–19; Robert Jackson, 34–35, 38–39, 52–59; Laurie Jordon, 20–31; Steve Marchesi, 122–131; John Mardon, 158–159; John Nez, 110–119; June Otani, 141,160–161, 245–256; Bill Purdom, 60–69; Susanna Spann, 73–85; Joe Veno, 96–109; Larry Winborg, 181–189.

Cover Photo: The Image Bank: © Sund.

Photo Credits: Peter Arnold, Inc.: © C. Allan Morgan, 92. © Art Resource: 163T. Bruce Coleman, Inc.: © Lee Foster, 41. © General Motors: 138. The Image Bank: © David Brownell, 8. The Image Works: © Mark Antman, 40T, 167, 168. Magnum Photos: © Rene Burri, 162. Monkmeyer Press Photo: © Paul Conklin, 40B; Pro Pix, 36. NASA Photo: 206, 207, 208L, R, 209. National Highway Traffic Safety Administration: 137. Photo Researchers, Inc.: © Van Bucher, 134; © Paolo Koch, 164–5; © Sarval, 169; © Science Photo Library, 120. Official U.S. Air Force Photograph: 211, 212, 213. Woodfin Camp & Associates: © George Hall, 37; © George Herben, 36–37; © Michal Heron, 166; © Sepp Seitz, 163B.

"Daedalus and Icarus" is adapted from STORIES OF THE GODS AND HEROES by Sally Benson. Copyright 1940 by Sally Benson, renewed 1968 by Sally Benson. Reprinted by permission of the publisher, Dial Books for Young Readers, a division of E. P. Dutton, Inc.

"Just Us Women" is abridged & adapted from JUST US WOMEN by Jeannette Caines, illustrated by Pat Cummings. Text Copyright © 1982 by Jeannette Franklin Caines. Illustrations Copyright © 1982 by Pat Cummings. By permission of Harper & Row, Publishers, Inc.

"Last Laugh" from KIM'S PLACE by Lee Bennett Hopkins. Text Copyright © 1974 by Lee Bennett Hopkins. Reprinted by permission of Curtis Brown, Ltd.

"Maria's Moon Walk" excerpted from MATTHEW LOONEY'S VOYAGE TO THE EARTH by Jerome Beatty. Copyright 1961. Reprinted by permission from Toni Mendez Inc.

"Miss Pickerell Goes to Mars" is from MISS PICKERELL GOES TO MARS by Ellen MacGregor. Copyright 1951 by Robert Noble MacGregor and John MacGregor. All Rights Reserved. Used by permission of McGraw-Hill Book Company.

"Moon" is from Poem # 737 in THE COMPLETE POEMS OF EMILY DICKINSON edited by Thomas A. Johnson. Reprinted by permission of Little, Brown & Co.

"Paddington Takes to the Road" is from PADDINGTON ABROAD by Michael Bond, Illustrated by Peggy Fortnum. Text Copyright © 1972 by Michael Bond. Illustrations Copyright © 1972 by Peggy Fortnum. Reprinted by permission of Houghton Mifflin Company and Curtis Brown, Ltd.

"Sun" from SMALL POEMS by Valerie Worth. Copyright © 1972 by Valerie Worth. Reprinted by permission of Farrar, Straus and Giroux, Inc.

"The Sun, The Moon, and The Stars" from TALES OF THE NIMIPOO by Eleanor B. Heady. Text Copyright © 1970 by Eleanor B. Heady. Reprinted by permission of Curtis Brown, Ltd.

"Travel" from COLLECTED POEMS by Edna St. Vincent Millay, published by Harper & Row, Publishers, Inc. Copyright 1921, 1948 by Edna St. Vincent Millay. Reprinted by permission.

"Voices" from AT THE TOP OF MY VOICE AND OTHER POEMS by Felice Holman. Copyright © 1970 by Felice Holman. Reprinted with the permission of Charles Scribner's Sons.

Contents

REACH FOR THE STARS

Preparing for Reading

Learning Vocabulary

Listen for the initial consonant.

house

horse	who	why	hoop
whose	where	while	whole

Read the sentences.

1. Whose book about the sun is this?
2. If you look at the sky, you will see the sun come up in the east and go down in the west.
3. The moon goes around the earth.
4. Sometimes the moon is in a line between the sun and the earth.

whose   east   west   moon

earth   between

Developing Background

Read and talk.

What is a Mystery?

A mystery story is fun to read. In a mystery, you must try to find out who did something and why. Sometimes there are scary things in a mystery and sometimes not. Sometimes you must read to the very last line of the story before you know what the mystery is. In "The Monday Mystery," a teacher and some children do an experiment. The earth, moon, and sun are in the mystery, and there is a party, too. What is the Monday mystery?

The Monday Mystery

Gibbs Davis

What was the experiment for today?

The class at West Rivers School looked on as Mr. Foley began to get all the things ready. There was a light for the sun, a big ball for the earth, and a small ball for the moon.

"The sun is a star. The earth moves around the sun," said Mr. Foley. He moved the big ball around the light.

"Miyo," called Mr. Foley. "Come up here and be the moon." He gave Miyo the small ball. "The moon moves around the earth. It goes this way," Mr. Foley said. Miyo moved the moon as Mr. Foley turned the earth.

Mr. Foley said, "Now, look. The moon will pass between the sun and the earth. The moon will be in a line with the earth and the sun. The light of the sun will not be seen from the earth. This is called a solar eclipse."

"The moon will do that?" said Josie. "The same old moon we see every night?"

"Yes," said Mr. Foley.

"Have you seen a solar eclipse before?" asked Gregg.

"Yes," said Mr. Foley, "but you must take care never to look right at an eclipse. It can hurt your eyes. This is the instrument we use to look at an eclipse. An eclipse is one of the very special and strange events on our earth. We will learn more about it soon."

The children went on to learn more about the sun, the moon, and the stars.

When Josie and Carol came back in from lunch that Friday, everything had been moved all around.

"Is this for an experiment, Mr. Foley?" asked Josie.

"This all goes with our Monday mystery," said Mr. Foley. "You will see something you have never seen before."

As Josie and Carol went home on the East/West school bus, they began to think about what Mr. Foley had said.

"I have to know, now," said Josie.

"Know what?" asked Carol.

"I have to find out what Mr. Foley's mystery is between now and Monday."

Carol found a newspaper on the bus. "Read this," she said. "Look at where it says 'Coming Events' for Monday."

"I think we are on the right track," said Josie, going through the newspaper.

"Whose picture is that?" asked Josie. "Whose photograph is on the front of the newspaper today?"

"The President," said Carol. "The reporters say that he's coming east to our city."

"We have never seen the President before," said Josie. "Do you think he's the mystery Mr. Foley was speaking of?"

"That might be it," said Carol. "All Mr. Foley said was that we will see something we have never seen before."

"We know two things about the mystery. We know the time and the place. It's on Monday and it's at school. We don't know what it is. It could be that the President is coming east to speak at our school."

"When we get home we can call Gregg. He might know more about the mystery."

Later they called Gregg. "Don't you remember that Mr. Foley said we might learn more about a solar eclipse very soon?" asked Gregg. "I think the Monday mystery is the solar eclipse."

"Yes," said Josie. "You may be right. I will think about it between now and Monday. Then we will see on Monday."

When Monday came the class was together. Everybody was excited but quiet.

"Today is the day," said Mr. Foley. "What you are about to see you will remember for a long time. The mystery is—"

"The President of the United States is coming to West Rivers School," Josie called out to the class.

"No," said Mr. Foley and went on, "the mystery has to do with the sun, the moon, and the earth. It's about time for our mystery to take place."

"I know what it is," said Gregg. "It is the solar eclipse."

"You are right," said Mr. Foley. "Remember that when the moon moves between the earth and the sun, we call it a solar eclipse."

All the children walked out of the school together. They looked at the solar eclipse through a special instrument. It was a strange thing to see the sky look as if it were night.

Everybody in the class was excited. In a little while, the sky began to grow lighter again.

Later when they went back in the school, Mr. Foley said, "Now, so that you will remember this day, it's time for our special solar eclipse party."

Everybody had a good time at the solar eclipse party.

"Whose turn is next for singing?" asked Mr. Foley. Carol said she wanted a turn. She began singing.

"When the moon comes
To take the sun away,
We have a party
For solar eclipse day."

"I don't think that today was a Monday mystery, Mr. Foley," said Josie.

"Then what was it?" asked Mr. Foley.

Josie had a big smile. "A 'Moonday' mystery!" she said, laughing.

Questions

Read and think.
1. What did the children see on Monday?
2. Who did Josie think they were going to see on Monday?
3. When does a solar eclipse take place?
4. Why did Gregg think that the Monday mystery was going to be a solar eclipse?

PREPARING FOR READING

Learning Vocabulary

Listen for the long vowel.

tree   pony

Read the sentences.

1. The animals got up <u>early</u>.
2. The ant said, "I must <u>warn</u> you that we will need food soon."
3. We need something to <u>burn</u> to make light.
4. "<u>Once</u> we have a light that will <u>rise</u> to make day and <u>set</u> to make night, we can find food," the animals said.

early   warn   burn   once
rise   set

Developing Background

Read and talk.

A Legend

Do you know how the turtle got its shell? In early times, a storyteller might have made up a story to tell about the turtle. Then the storyteller could pass the story on to his or her children who did the same with their children. The story went on in this way for a long time. A story like this is called a legend. As time went by, people might write the legend down so that everybody could read it.

"The Sun, the Moon, and the Stars" is a legend. As you read, try to imagine how a storyteller might tell this legend.

The Sun, The Moon, And The Stars

ELEANOR HEADY

Adapted by Margaret H. Lippert

Once, when the earth began, there was no light. It was always night. It was hard for the animals to walk around because there was no light to help them see. It was hard for them to find food to eat.

Now at this time a chief lived in the sky over the earth. This chief had three children, two boys and a girl.

One day the girl said to her younger brother, "It is always night. I don't like night all the time. I wish we could have some light."

"I think we can make some light," said
her brother. "Come with me down to the
earth. We will look for something to burn.
Then we will have light."

So they went together down a huge pine
tree to the earth, and they looked around for
something good to burn. They found some
small pine trees on the ground. They made
these trees into a big ball. Then they went
back up to the sky with the big pine ball.
They walked on to the east, where the sky
began.

"Light the ball," said the younger
brother. "It will burn well. I will take it
across the sky. It will make light for you
and all the animals on the earth."

The sister did light the big pine ball. As the brother went across the sky, the animals saw the light rise in the east.

"Look at that big light coming up in the east," they said. "Now we can see!"

They were so happy that they went racing around looking for food. But before they could find the food they needed, the boy had run across the sky to the west.

"The light is going," the animals screamed. "Come back, come back!"

But the light set in the west. There was no light again, and the animals were sad.

"We will go and talk to the chief," they said. "We must tell him that we need the light for a longer time."

The animals went up the huge pine tree
to see the chief, who was in his tepee with
his children. Coyote spoke to the chief.

"Your son gave us light," said Coyote, "and we came up to thank him for it. But we need light longer. He went too fast. He set too early. Please tell him to go slowly so that we can have light for a longer time."

The chief spoke to his younger son and asked him to move slowly across the sky.

"What can I do?" asked his son. "If I go slowly, the pine ball will burn up before I can get over to the west."

Then his sister said, "I think I can help you. When you get very high I will take a new big pine ball up to you. Then we can light that new ball. You can take the new ball slowly to the west, so the animals on the earth will have light for a longer time."

"I am proud of you, my daughter," said the chief. "That should work."

The animals were excited. Coyote said,
"From now on, your son will be called He Who
Goes All Over the Sky, and your daughter
will be called She Who Helps the Sun."

Every day after that the younger son and his sister made the sun rise and give light to the animals who lived on the earth.

Now all this time, the older son was sleeping in the tepee. One night, his father went to him.

"Your brother and sister work hard every day," he said. "They get up early. They make the sun rise and set. You sleep all the time. Get up and think of something you can do to help them. I will warn you once, but I will not warn you again."

The older son did not like what his father said. "You will not have to warn me again," he said. "I will think of something."

He began to think.

The younger son came into the tepee. He put the pine ball down. He was very tired after his long day, and went to sleep. As he was sleeping, some sparks flew up from his pine ball, through the opening in the top of the tepee. The sparks turned into stars. The older son saw this.

"I have it!" he said. "I know what I can do. I am going to the east. I will walk across the sky at night. Once I get high over the tepee where my brother is sleeping, I will stop. The light from his pine ball will come up to me through the opening in the top of the tepee. It will light me. Then, I will give my light to the earth at night."

That night, the animals looked up at the sky and saw a new light. "Look," they said. "There is a new light now, a light for the night!"

"We will call this light He Who Comes Out Early," Coyote said, "because he is up before day."

So now the animals have light in the day and light at night. They are happy.

The chief is proud of all his children, He Who Goes All Over the Sky, She Who Helps the Sun, and He Who Comes Out Early, because they give light to the earth, in the day and at night.

Questions

Read and think.

1. What did the girl and her younger brother burn to make light?
2. What did the animals want the younger son to do?
3. What did the sparks from the ball turn into?
4. Why was the father not happy with his older son?

SUN

The sun
Is a leaping fire
Too hot
To go near,

But it will still
Lie down
In warm yellow squares
On the floor

Like a flat
Quilt, where
The cat can curl
And purr.

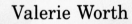

Valerie Worth

MOON

The moon was but a chin of gold
   A night or two ago,
And now she turns her perfect face
   Upon the world below.

        Emily Dickinson

PREPARING FOR READING

Learning Vocabulary

Listen for the long vowel.

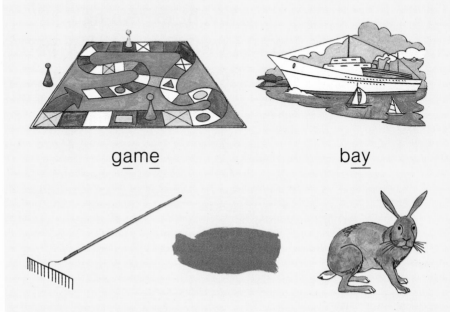

game   bay

Read the sentences.

1. In cold weather, people stay in the house.
2. They need a useful way to supply energy to their homes.
3. If they had a collector, they could use the heat of the sun for energy.

stay   useful   supply   energy
collector   heat

Developing Background

Read and talk.

No Heat

Imagine that it is a very, very cold day. The temperature is going down. You come into the house from school, but it is as cold in the house as it is out in the snow. There is no heat in the world.

All the coal, gas, oil, and trees that have been useful for heating are not there. Could this be true? It could be, if we do not try to use energy with care. In "Energy from the Sun," you will read about a kind of energy we can use for heating. Can we use up this kind of energy, too?

GAS

OIL

ENERGY FROM THE SUN

JOHN USS

In the summer, it sometimes gets very hot. The temperature may stay very high. Then we think about how to get away from the heat. We may go to the ocean or to the mountains.

In the winter, the weather is very different. It sometimes gets very cold. The temperature goes down. People stay in the house much of the time. They want to keep warm. They must find a way to heat their homes to keep out the cold.

People use different things found in the earth to supply heat. These things may be gas, oil, or coal. We can burn gas, oil, or coal to supply heat. Each of these things is a useful supply of energy. But we may not always have all the gas, oil, and coal we need to supply us with energy. They may run out someday.

For a long time people have looked for a new supply of energy for heating their homes. They have turned to solar energy. Solar energy is energy from the sun. Today, more and more people find solar energy a useful way to help heat their homes.

The picture helps show you how we use solar energy to heat a house. Look at the picture to learn how solar heating works.

A solar collector can be put on the roof of a house. The collector can take heat from the sun. The heat from the collector will pass to water that runs under the collector. The water will then move to a place with more water or rocks that will store the heat. The water or rocks here will stay hot a long time. Air can blow over the rocks or water and move the heat through the house.

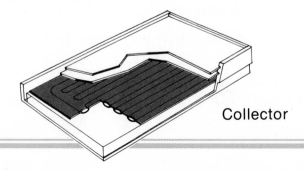

Collector

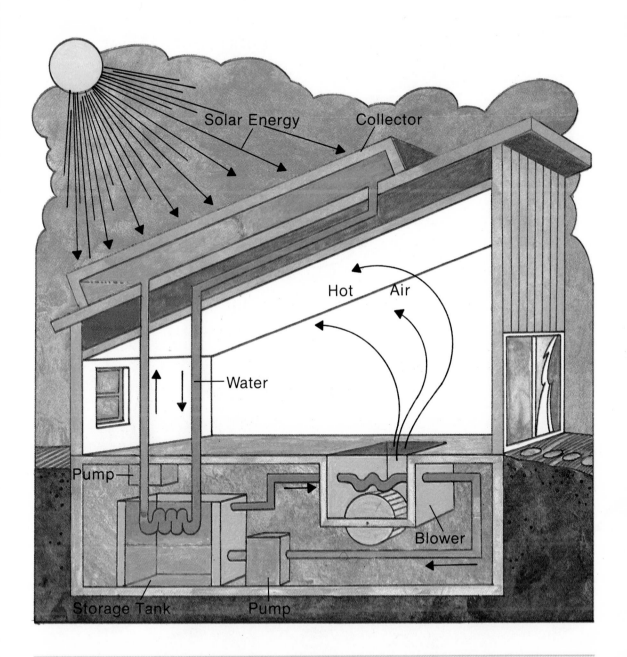

In places where the sun is strong for much of the year, solar energy alone can heat a house. In places where the sun is not as strong, solar energy can work together with gas, oil, or coal to keep our homes warm.

As the supply of gas, oil, and coal runs out, solar energy will be more and more important for heating. It may turn out to be a very useful and important supply of energy for us in time to come.

Questions

Read and think.

1. What kind of energy can come from the sun?
2. Where can you put a solar collector?
3. Where can solar energy alone heat a house?
4. Why do people want to find a new energy supply that does not use gas, oil, or coal?

PREPARING FOR READING

Learning Vocabulary

Listen for the contraction.

$$I + will = I'll$$
$$she + will = she'll$$
$$he + will = he'll$$

Read the sentences.

1. Now we'll read a story about a fearless father and son who were not afraid to fly.
2. They soared high in the sky on wings made of feathers and wax.
3. When the wax melted, what do you think they could have done?

we'll   fearless   afraid   soared
feathers   wax   melted

Developing Background

Read and talk.

Flying On Your Own

When people saw fearless birds flying in the sky, they wanted to fly on their own, too. First they made wings. When the wings didn't work, they made a ship that could fly. A tiny airplane was one of the first things that people flew in. The huge flying boat flew one time and then was put away. Now people can fly on their own in space with some special help.

"Daedalus and Icarus" is a story from early times about a man and his son and their wish to fly.

DAEDALUS AND ICARUS

Retold by
Karen Young

Year after year, Daedalus and his son Icarus worked on buildings on the island of Crete. When the king of Crete wanted a new castle, Daedalus and Icarus were called in to work on it.

The king was happy with their work.

"This is a beautiful castle!" the king said. "It sits high and proud over the island. Because of it, all of the people will know of my power."

Then the king asked Daedalus and Icarus to make him a special maze under the castle. It was there that the king wanted to keep a strange animal with huge claws and big teeth.

This maze was very scary. Those people the king did not like had to walk into it. They were afraid because they couldn't find the trail out.

But a young man called Theseus wasn't afraid. He did away with the huge animal. Then he found his way out of the maze under the castle.

The king found out about Theseus. He couldn't keep his feelings quiet. He began roaring, "This is because of you, Daedalus! Now that your work is done, I know you want to go from this island, but I will use my power to make you stay here always. You can never go from here!"

"We'll never get off this island," said Icarus to Daedalus.

Day after day, they looked across the water, but no boat came for them. How much they wanted to go away from the island and its king!

Then one day as Icarus looked over the water, he saw a bird. It soared into the sky.

"That bird is fearless," Icarus said. "It can fly away. I wish we had wings to fly away, too."

After a while, Daedalus said, "We can have wings! Now hear me, my son. Pick up all the feathers you can find, as fast as you can. We'll find a way to make wings and fly off this island."

Day after day, Daedalus melted wax and Icarus found the feathers. With the wax, Daedalus stuck the feathers together to make wings.

Soon the day came when the wings were ready. There were wings for Daedalus and wings for Icarus.

"Put on these wings," Daedalus said to Icarus. Then Daedalus put his wings on, too. "Now we must try to fly," he said.

"We'll fly through the air like birds," called Icarus. Icarus was excited. "Now I, too, will be fearless!"

It was time to go.

"Icarus!" Daedalus called. "Remember to fly slowly, or your wings will not last. Fly high, or you will fall into the water. But take care not to fly too high, or the wax on your wings will be melted by the heat of the sun."

Icarus was fearless. He wasn't afraid to fly over the castle of the king. Icarus was not afraid to fly over the water.

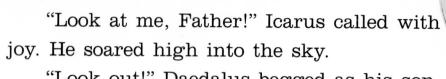

"Look at me, Father!" Icarus called with joy. He soared high into the sky.

"Look out!" Daedalus begged as his son soared. "Remember my words to you. Stay away from the sun!"

Icarus didn't listen to Daedalus. Soon the sun melted the wax on his wings. Feathers began to fly from his wings.

"Father," screamed Icarus. "Help me, I am falling." Down, down, down went Icarus.

"My son! My son!" Daedalus called, but he could not help. Icarus was lost.

A sad Daedalus flew back to the island of Crete.

When he lost his son, Daedalus lost everything. For him the joy of flying was over.

Questions

Read and think.

1. What did Daedalus and Icarus want to do?
2. How did Daedalus make wings?
3. Why did Daedalus and Icarus need to take care not to fly too high?
4. Why did Icarus fly too high?

PREPARING FOR READING

Learning Vocabulary
Listen for the long vowel.

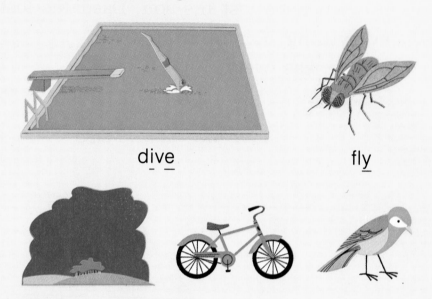

dive   fly

Read the sentences.

1. What is the best <u>size</u> <u>tube</u> for making a telescope?
2. When you <u>hold</u> the tube to your eyes, will you see things <u>clearly</u>?
3. In this story, Sally will read <u>directions</u> for making an instrument that will help her look at the stars.

size   tube   hold
clearly   directions

Developing Background

Read and talk.

Directions

"We need directions for the experiment you did in class," your friends say. How can you give directions clearly? Give directions for the experiment one step at a time, by going over what to do first, next, and then last in the experiment. Tell your friends everything they will need to know every step of the way. Then if you need to, go over the directions one more time.

In the next story, "Making a Telescope," Sally read directions so she could make a telescope.

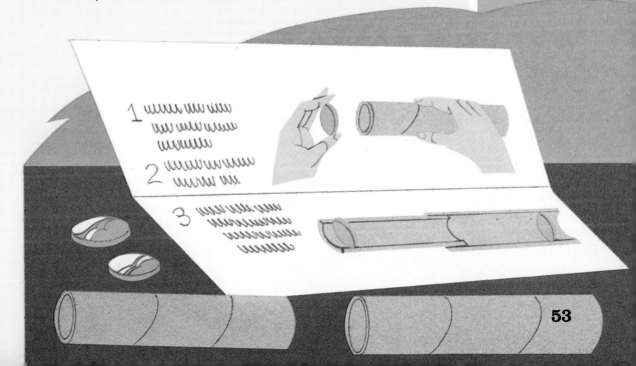

MAKING A
TELESCOPE

JOHN USS

A telescope is an instrument that you can use to see the stars more clearly and to learn about the night sky. The very first telescope was put together in the early 1600's. Soon after, a man called Galileo Galilei made his own telescope and began to use it to look at the moon and the stars. Can you imagine the feelings he had when he looked at the night sky through his telescope for the first time?

With his telescope, Galileo began to learn what the moon is like. He found out that the Milky Way is made up of many, many stars.

One kind of telescope we use today is like Galileo's telescope. A huge telescope of this kind is at the Yerkes Observatory in Wisconsin.

Sally had read about the telescope at Yerkes Observatory. She wanted to see the moon and stars more clearly. Sally and her mother made a visit to a museum. Sally saw a kit called *How to Make a Telescope* at the museum store. Her mother got the kit for her. Sally found directions in the kit. The directions said what she should do to make a telescope.

First Sally found two tubes in the kit. The size of each tube was about the same. Two different kinds of lenses were in the kit. The lenses were the right size to go into the tubes.

Sally could hold both tubes at the same time. Then she could slowly slide the first tube into the second. Now the tubes were together. Next, Sally put one of the lenses in one tube and one in the second tube. Now Sally could hold the telescope up to her eye and look through it at something across the way. She could move the tubes in and out so she could see clearly. Everything looked very big in size.

Sally could take the telescope out at night and use it to look at the moon and the stars. It helped her to have a map of the stars. She found a sky map in her newspaper.

The sky map showed Sally the important star pictures in the night sky. The star pictures looked like animals, things, or people. A star book showed Sally what each star picture was called. It said in what directions she should look to find the different stars. Then Sally could hold her telescope and find the star pictures in the sky, look at the Milky Way, or find a special star.

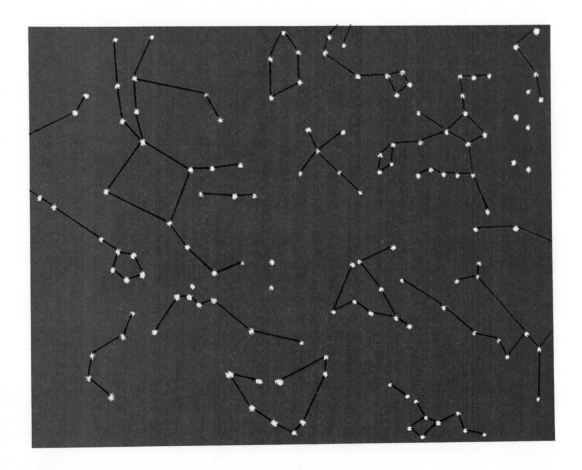

People like Sally have always found mystery in the stars. They have looked at stars and have been excited by them. With her telescope, Sally found looking at the stars a new and different hobby.

Questions

Read and think.
1. What can a telescope help you do?
2. Who was one of the first people to use the telescope?
3. What is a sky map?
4. How did Sally make her own telescope?

PREPARING FOR READING

Learning Vocabulary

Listen for the initial consonant.

rug

write	water	wring	wrap
radio	wrote	wings	red

Read the sentences.

1. Grandma was never <u>wrong</u> about the woods.
2. She <u>knew</u> the place in the woods where the sun <u>shines</u> <u>brightly</u>.
3. She knew how to find north and <u>south</u> as well as east and west if you were lost.

wrong   knew   shines   brightly   south

Developing Background

Read and talk.

Stars and More Stars

On a beautiful night with no clouds and no lights around you, millions of stars can be seen clearly with a telescope.

What is a star? A star is a body in space that can make its own light. Our own sun is a star. The stars are millions of miles away. Our own sun is 93,000,000 miles away. The next star to our sun is so many miles away it may take more than a year for its light to get to earth. In "Look to the Stars," Grandma teaches the children how to look for pictures in the stars.

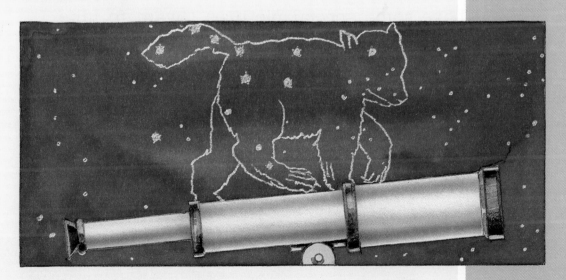

LOOK TO THE
S·T·A·R·S

CAROL CARRICK

Kara and Meg wanted Grandma to take them to the movies.

"Please!" they begged her.

"That is the wrong place to be on a pretty spring night like this. We can go to the movies on a night when it is raining. I have some special pictures I want to take you to see," said Grandma.

"Where are they?" asked Meg.

"These are pictures you have to look for in the night sky," said Grandma.

"I want to see pictures, too," said Ted, jumping like a grasshopper. Ted was Kara and Meg's little brother.

Kara and Meg knew that time with Grandma was always fun. Grandma was always ready to show them important things about their world.

"Each of you get a sleeping bag," said Grandma.

"Are we going to camp out?" asked Meg.

"Not this time," said Grandma. "The sleeping bag is for you to sit on so you don't get cold."

Kara and Meg looked at Grandma. Where could they be going? It was a mystery to them.

Grandma and the children walked down the road in back of their farm. The night was so black that it was hard for them to see. Grandma turned on a light for them as they walked. After some time they went by a swamp.

"I know where we are now by the music," said Grandma. The frogs were singing loudly.

Something moved in the brush down by the road.

"What was that?" said Meg. She was afraid.

"A little mouse or something," said Kara. Kara liked to act fearless.

Then a bat flew out of the woods and Meg screamed.

Kara laughed. "Hold on to me if you are scared."

When they came to a high place in the road, Grandma said, "Duck under this fence."

"Take care not to trip," she called. "On a night when the moon shines brightly, you can't see my pictures very well."

At last they were at the field. They each put down a sleeping bag to sit on.

"The best place to see stars is from space," said Grandma. "But millions of people have looked up from a field like this and seen the same pictures."

"The pictures are in the stars," Kara said to Ted.

"Wrong!" said Ted. "Those are not pictures at all."

"They make pictures if you learn how to look at them," said Grandma. "You have to imagine a line running from star to star. Before the telescope, people did not know what stars were and they were afraid of them. It made them feel better to see the stars as pictures of things they knew about and to give them each a story."

"Why couldn't we look at the stars at home?" asked Meg. "Why did we have to come out here?"

"It's hard to see as many stars when a light shines brightly from a house or street," said Grandma.

"If there are millions of stars up there, how can we find the special stars that make pictures?" asked Kara.

"That will take a little practice," said Grandma. "Here I have something that will help us. This is a telescope I had when I was a girl. First we will look with our eyes. Then you may want to look with the telescope. Look, that is the Big Dipper, and over there is the Little Dipper."

"That star shines so brightly," said Meg, looking south. "What is it called?"

"That star is said to be the heart of the Lion."

"It does not look like a lion to me," said Ted.

"I'm afraid not all of them make good pictures," said Grandma. "I'll make a map for you when we get home so you can find some more pictures."

The first star you should look for is the North Star. It's right there in the Little Dipper. The special thing about the North Star is that you will always see it in the same place. When you find it, you can get your directions from it. If you look at the North Star, you are looking north. East will be to your right and west will be to your left. If your back is to the North Star, you are looking south.

Then Grandma looked at the sky and said, "How about that! It's after 9."

"How could you see the time by looking at the sky?" asked Meg.

"That is the second mystery for the night," said Grandma, and she laughed.

"Come on!" said the children.

"All right. I knew because the Big Dipper goes around the North Star and tells the time. Right now, it's time to go home."

Kara got up. She knew her house was to the south of where the field was. To find south, she knew she must turn her back on the North Star.

"I can't go wrong from now on," she said, "as long as the North Star shines."

Questions

Read and think.

1. What special pictures did Grandma take Kara, Meg, and Ted to see?
2. If you look north, what star will you see?
3. How did Grandma use the sky to tell time?
4. How has the telescope helped people to learn more about space?

WRITING ACTIVITY

WRITE A LEGEND

Prewrite

The story in this book called "The Sun, the Moon, and the Stars" is a legend. It tells how the sun, the moon, and the stars came to be in the sky. Grandma liked star pictures in the story "Look to the Stars." Did you know that the Big Dipper is in a bigger star picture called the Big Bear? There is a star picture called the Swan, too. You are going to write a legend about a star picture.

Try to imagine why star pictures are in the sky. Did the Swan fly too high? Is the Big Dipper there for Big Bear to use when he wants a drink?

Here are some directions to help you get ready to write.

1. Pick a star picture for your legend.
2. Remember a legend must tell who, what, and why. Write some sentences that tell what will take place first, second, third, and so on in your legend.

Write

1. Read your sentences from page 70.
2. How many paragraphs will you have in your legend? Your first paragraph could tell about the people or animals in your legend. Your next paragraphs could tell why the star pictures are in the sky.
3. Start each paragraph with a sentence that tells what it is about.
4. Use the sentences you wrote for page 70.
5. Use your Glossary for help with spelling.

Revise

Read your legend. Do your sentences tell what the star picture is and why it is in the sky? Does each paragraph talk about one thing? If not, rewrite what you need to now.

1. Did you indent the first word in each paragraph?
2. Did you use correct end punctuation for each sentence?
3. Did you capitalize the names of people and special animals?

PREPARING FOR READING

Learning Vocabulary

Listen for the contraction.

he + had = he'd

he + would = he'd

she + had = she'd

she + would = she'd

Read the sentences.

1. They'd found the road to freedom.
2. They'd take a special railroad north.
3. This railroad made no sound, but the many people riding it reached a place where they could be free at last.

they'd   freedom   railroad   sound
reached   free

Developing Background

Read and talk.

A Special Railroad

At one time in the United States, black people were slaves. Harriet Tubman was a slave. The story "Harriet Tubman" is about her and what she did to get her freedom. The story will tell you about a special railroad. This railroad had stations and made stops, but it was a strange railroad, too. The people who worked for it did not want all the people to know what they were doing. They wanted the slaves looking for freedom to know. How did Harriet use her freedom to help slaves travel on the strange and special railroad?

HARRIET TUBMAN

Rita M. Howard

Five people were in the swamp that black night. The noise of riders, and the sound of rushing water were all around them. Little Nat's heart was racing. His body was as cold as ice. But he didn't make a sound. Nat, his mother, his father, and an old woman were running away from slavery. Night riders wanted to find them and return them to slavery. Harriet Tubman wanted them to travel the trail to a place where they'd be free. They were on the underground railroad.

The underground railroad had no train cars. It had no track. It was a trail that people walked from the South to the North. In time they'd come to Pennsylvania. Pennsylvania was in the North. It was a place where slaves could be free. Harriet Tubman was the fearless woman who could take the slaves to the North.

The slaves did not travel when the sun was out. In the day, they'd hide and sleep on the ground. Their food was the small animals that Harriet Tubman might find for them in the woods.

Sometimes there were stops on the underground railroad. The stops were at the homes of friends of Harriet Tubman. These friends wanted to help everybody to be free. At the stops, the tired slaves could eat and rest. Nat's family was going to stay at the home of John Tucker the next day. His home was one of the stops on the trail of the underground railroad.

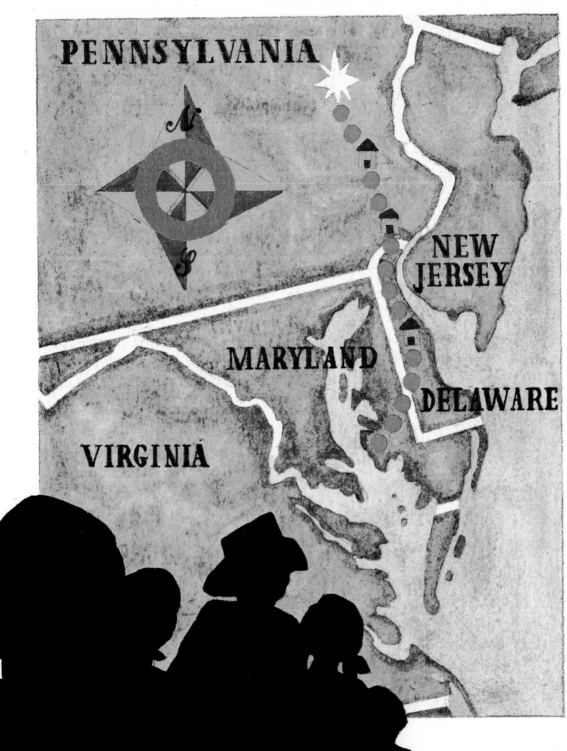

Harriet Tubman began to move the family from the swamp. It was hard to walk because the swamp was like a pool of wet land. Nat's family could not see where they were going. They walked slowly. No one was speaking. Nat was scared and tired. He needed to know if they were lost.

After a time they reached hard ground. Harriet Tubman looked up at the sky. There were millions of stars. Harriet turned around and around, and then she saw the star she was looking for.

"There it is," she said. "There is the North Star. It points to a land that is free. It points to freedom. If we keep it in front of us and on our left, we'll be on the track to a free land."

Harriet Tubman could read the sky like a map. As long as she could see the stars, they were not lost.

They began to walk again.

"Keep your eye on the North Star," Harriet said. And they did.

That night they reached the home of John Tucker. Tucker gave them food and then they went to bed, tired from their long night.

After lunch the next day, Nat said to Harriet Tubman, "How did you come to do this work on the underground railroad?"

Harriet Tubman said to Nat that she had been a slave, too. She spoke about how the underground railroad began. Her home was on a big farm in Dorchester County, Maryland. Work, work, work. Hard work was what she did all day, every day. Soon she was very strong. But she was not happy. She wanted a better way to live. She wanted to be free.

Harriet spoke to her brothers about an underground railroad. There was no one to show them the way. But Harriet wanted to try. She wanted to walk to freedom. Her brothers said they wanted to try, too.

One night, while everybody on the farm was sleeping, Harriet and her brothers left home. The sound of animals came to them in the night. Then came the scary sound of night riders and a dog. They were coming after them. They were on the trail of Harriet and her brothers.

Run! Hide! Run and hide! Run through the woods, Harriet! Hide in the swamp, brothers!

The brothers began to feel scared and
tired. Their muscles hurt from so much
running. They could not go on. They begged
Harriet to return to the farm, and to slavery.

Harriet said, "No!"

The brothers turned back. Harriet went on.
She had to be free.

Then Harriet was alone. But the stars, the sun, and the moon were her friends. The moon gave light so she could see at night. The stars moved across the sky from east to west. Harriet knew them and how they moved. They helped her know the time at night. The sun helped her know the time in the day.

One star was a special friend. It did not move across the sky. Polaris, the North Star, was always in the north. It helped her recall the way.

With the North Star always in front of her, Harriet walked across Maryland and Delaware. At last she reached Pennsylvania, the place where she could be free.

Soon Harriet had new friends in her new home, but she missed her family and her old friends. She wanted them to be free too.

Again and again, Harriet went south to help the slaves travel the underground railroad to freedom.

"No one should be a slave," she said. Now with the underground railroad, Harriet Tubman found a new way to help people to be free.

That night, Nat and his family went on their way north. They had a long, hard trip before them. But they had one of the best people to help them walk to freedom. They had Harriet Tubman.

Questions

Read and think.
1. What was the underground railroad?
2. What did Harriet Tubman use to help her find where north was?
3. Where did the slaves stop to rest and eat?
4. Why did Nat feel afraid as he and his family walked north?

PREPARING FOR READING

Learning Vocabulary

Listen for the contraction.

they + had = they'd

they + would = they'd

I + had = I'd

I + would = I'd

Read the sentences.

1. You'd think it was quiet in space, only you'd be wrong.

2. Waves of sound make prints that only a special kind of telescope can see and hear.

you'd   only   waves   prints

Developing Background

Read and talk.

Sound

Sound is all around us. People will scream loudly for their team at a soccer game. The sound of a crying kitten is very quiet. Look at the table. Can you think of one more loud or quiet sound to put in the table?

A Table of Sound	
A LOUD SOUND	A QUIET SOUND
Thunder	Snow
A plane ready to take off	A blimp

In "Listening in Outer Space," you will read how people listen for sound in a special way.

LISTENING IN OUTER SPACE

SALLY SENZELL

It is a quiet night. The light from billions of tiny stars go on and off in the night sky.

You may think there is not a sound in the sky. But that is not true. Let us think about and imagine all the sound that does travel through the night sky.

Sound comes in waves. These waves bounce off the earth, and travel in many different directions at one time. Because of this, sound can reach people in different places. Some of the sound waves in space come from people on earth. It may be from a TV show or a call.

How can this sound travel from place to place? It can travel with the help of a satellite. Let us say that people are making a TV show in California. The sound and pictures from the show go up to a satellite in outer space.

The sound and pictures bounce off the satellite and travel back down to earth. The different TV stations around the world can then pick up the sound and pictures from the satellite. The show from California can be seen all over the world.

Before there were satellites, it was very hard to learn about things that went on in different places around the world. Now we can hear about them right away.

Today people are calling places they could not reach before satellites. At one time we could make calls only to some places in the world. The calls had to travel through a line. There were many places the line did not reach. Some calls had to travel through a line under the water. Sometimes you'd not hear the people clearly. But today millions of calls can travel clearly from country to country by satellite.

Imagine you are going for a walk by the water. You can look back and see where you have walked, by looking at the prints your feet have made. Sound in space can make prints, too. We can't see these prints, but we can hear them.

Now let us think about the sound in space that does not come from people. Sometimes the sun can make a "huh-huh" sound. Some stars make only an "s-s-s" sound, but some stars make a roaring noise. The sound is there, but, as much as you'd try, you could not hear this sound yourself. You'd have to have a special telescope to hear this sound. The special telescope that can pick up this sound in space is called a radio telescope.

As you know, a telescope helps us to see the moon and stars. A radio telescope helps people find out about places in space that we can't see. There are billions of stars that can't be seen with the best telescope, but their sound can reach the radio telescope. It can pick up special sound from these stars. Then it can turn the special sound into a new sound that we can hear.

The radio telescope tells us many things. It tells us the temperature of stars. It tells us how long it might take to travel to different stars. The radio telescope has helped us find new stars.

Some people want to use the radio telescope to listen to outer space. They want to know what kinds of things there are in outer space. Are there people? Are there animals? Could our sound reach the stars? Some people think it can. For now, we do not know, we can only listen.

The radio telescope may help us learn more about the mystery of sound in space.

Questions

Read and think.

1. What can help sound travel from one place to many different places around the world?
2. Before there were satellites, how did calls have to travel?
3. What special telescope can pick up sound?
4. How does a satellite help sound travel from place to place?

VOICES

There are songs and sounds
in stillness
In the quiet after dark,
Sounds within sounds,
Songs within songs.
There are rhythms in the quiet
And pulses in the night,
Beats within beats,
Drums within drums.

Something calling in the embers,
Something crying in the rocks,
And out beyond the darkness
There are voices in the stars.

Felice Holman

PREPARING FOR READING

Learning Vocabulary

Listen for the initial consonant.

fish

frog   photo   fox

phone   foot   fly

Read the sentences.
1. You can <u>phone</u> from your <u>ship</u> to the <u>shore</u> if you have the right kind of phone.
2. The radio <u>operator</u> can help you place your call.
3. Could that operator place your call if you were about to <u>sail</u> on a <u>rocket</u> into space?

phone   ship   shore   operator
sail   rocket

Developing Background

Read and talk.

A Letter

May 7, 19___

Dear Grandpa,

We are doing a play at school. Will you come? It is called "SOS from Outer Space." It is about some strange space people. I will be Zeeva, a girl from outer space. Eron, Lunar, and Talo are my space friends. An SOS is a radio call that people on a ship use when they need help. That is all I will tell you about the play. Please come on May 10, at 2:00 P.M.

Pam

S.O.S.
FROM OUTER SPACE

SUSAN NANUS

Players
Ana, a girl
Paco, a boy
Eron, a boy from Outer Space
Zeeva, a girl from Outer Space
Lunar, the man in the moon
Talo, a radio operator in Outer Space

Setting
At the shore

A radio is over on one side
of the shore.

(Paco and Ana come running in.
They do not see Eron and Zeeva,
who are at a different place on
the shore.)

99

Paco: See, Ana? There is no one here. You must have been dreaming.

Ana: I was not dreaming, Paco. I did hear people calling for help. I did hear an SOS.

Paco: But Ana, who could be calling? There is no one on this shore.

(They hear calling.)

Eron: My. . . ship! Help! SOS! SOS!

Ana: Paco! Did you hear that?

Paco: You did overhear something before, Ana.

Zeeva: Oh! Where am I? Hello? Operator? Come in, please.

Ana: She said, "Operator."

Paco: Ana, I think I know what we are listening to. It is a call for help from a ship to shore radio.

Ana: You are right! A boat must be stuck or lost in a storm.

Paco: We must get to a phone and try calling for help.

(Zeeva and Eron slowly get up. At first, Ana and Paco do not see them. Then, Ana and Paco look at Zeeva and Eron.)

Eron: Hello, friends. We have come a long way. Is this the moon?

Paco: Say that again, please.

Eron: Is this the moon, my friend?

Paco: No. It isn't. But who are you?

Zeeva: I'm Zeeva, and he is Eron. Are we on a star?

Paco: No. You are on Earth.

Zeeva and Eron: *(Together)* Earth?

Eron: Oh Zeeva, we are so lost!

Paco: Where do you come from?

Eron: Well, I think you people on Earth call it "Outer Space."

Ana and Paco: Outer Space?

Ana: How did you get here?

Eron: Well, the last thing I remember was sailing on our rocket through the air.

Zeeva: Here is our radio. We have to try calling Talo, our radio operator, at home.

Eron: Hello? Talo? Come in, Talo!

Zeeva: This is a very special radio, my friend. On this radio you can hear and see the people you are talking to.

Talo: I can hear you, Eron. I know you were lost sailing your ship. Where did you land?

Eron: On a shore some place on Earth.

Talo: Earth? Oh, my!

Eron: I know, I know. It wasn't very good sailing. Can you give us some directions?

Talo: All right. First, sail to the North Star . . .

(They look at the radio. Talo is not there.)

Eron: Talo? Talo? Come in! Oh, no!

Paco: What is wrong?

Eron: I lost him!

Ana: Can't you phone him again?

Zeeva: There is no phone. As we said before, this is a special radio. The only way to reach Talo is to imagine him.

Paco: Imagine him?

Eron: Yes, but Zeeva and I are not very good at that. At home, we don't have to imagine very much.

Ana: Well, try, Eron. If you don't try, you might never get home.

(Eron looks away. Lunar comes on the radio.)

Lunar: Did I overhear you say you are lost?

Zeeva: You are not Talo!

Lunar: I should hope not! I am Lunar, the man in the moon. And who are you people?

Ana: We are two children from Earth and two people from Outer Space.

Lunar: And what do you want from me?

Zeeva: We don't want you at all. We want to get directions from Talo.

Lunar: You don't want me? But I am your light in the night sky. Well, all right then. I'll be on my way.

(Lunar goes away)

Zeeva: You see? When we imagine something, it doesn't always work out.

Ana: Paco and I can help you find Talo.

Zeeva: How can you do that?

Ana: If Paco and I imagine Talo with you, we will reach him.

Paco: Yes! I like to imagine things. We do it all the time, when we play.

Eron: Well, if you think it will help. . . .

Ana: Come on, Eron. We will all imagine Talo together.

(They all hide their eyes and think hard.)

Ana, Paco, Eron and Zeeva: *(Together)* Talo, Talo, please come in!

(Talo comes on the radio.)

Talo: Hello? Eron?

Paco: We did it!

Eron: Yes, Talo. We lost you before, but now you are here. Give us the directions, please.

Talo: Yes. First, sail your ship to the North Star. Then go left and keep flying. Go left again, and then you are home.

Zeeva: Thank you, Talo.

Talo: Over and out.

(Talo goes out.)

Zeeva: Thank you, Ana and Paco, for all your help. We couldn't have found Talo if you didn't help us to imagine him. We want to give you something to thank you. This will help you to always reach us in Outer Space.

Ana and Paco: (*Excited*) What is it?

Eron: Our special radio. Now you can speak to us from Earth. We will always be good friends.

Ana and Paco: Oh! Thank you!

Eron: Come on, Zeeva. It is time to sail home.

Zeeva: Thank you for all your help, Ana and Paco. We were lost, but we found good friends on Earth.

Paco: But where is your rocket ship?

Eron: Over there on the shore.

Paco: Where? I am looking, but I don't see it.

Eron: Oh it's a special rocket ship, Paco. You have to imagine it. So long!

(Zeeva and Eron run off to sail home.)

Ana: Well, Paco. There was an SOS after all.

Paco: Yes, but it was an SOS from Outer Space!

Questions

Read and think.

1. Where did Eron and Zeeva come from?
2. Why did Eron and Zeeva need to call Talo?
3. How did Paco and Ana help Eron and Zeeva?
4. Why couldn't Eron and Zeeva imagine Talo on their own?

PREPARING FOR READING

Learning Vocabulary

Listen for the long vowels.

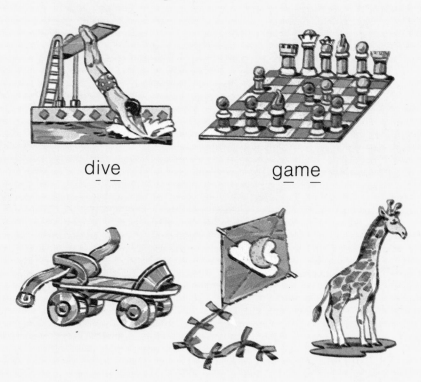

dive   game

Read the sentences.

1. Children can <u>glide</u> through space on the moon.

2. <u>We'd</u> never be <u>late</u> to school.

3. We might need a weight with a <u>handle</u> to hold us down on the moon.

glide   we'd   late   handle

Developing Background

Read and talk.

The Moon

People from the United States have been on the moon. You may have seen pictures of them walking and jumping very high. Why can they jump so high on the moon? Gravity is the pull that earth is always making on a body. On earth, when you jump up in the air, you will come down fast because of earth's strong gravity. The moon's gravity is not as strong as earth's, so people can jump very high. In "Maria's Moon Walk," you will read about how too little gravity did something scary to Maria.

Maria's Moon Walk

Jerome Beatty, Jr.

Matt and his sister Maria were going to their bowling class. If Matt and Maria were on Earth, they might walk to bowling class as we do. But Matt and Maria lived on the moon where there is little gravity. The gravity helped them glide slowly to class.

Maria was holding the big black bowling ball, as she and Matt left. They were late for bowling class, but they had to move very slowly. There was so little gravity on the moon that it was hard for things to stay down. If they moved too fast, they could get velocipitis and float right up in the air.

So boys and girls who lived on the moon had to take care not to move too fast. But with all the running and jumping that children like to do, it was hard for them to remember not to move fast all the time.

Many a time you might see a mother or a father come with a rope to help get their floating children down.

"Maria," said Matt, "we'd better try not to be late today. We will have to glide a little faster to get there on time. Here, let me hold the bowling ball for you."

Maria gave the ball to Matt as they went rushing down the street. Matt went as fast as he could, and Maria began to skip. After a skip or two, Maria found that she was floating up and up. Soon she was not next to Matt.

"Help me, Matt! Help me!" she screamed as she went up away from Matt.

Matt began to reach out, but he could not get hold of Maria. Why didn't he remember how important it was for her to have the bowling ball? He knew now that she needed the bowling ball to hold her down. Maria needed the weight of the ball because there is so little gravity on the moon. It was velocipitis!

When Matt looked up, he saw Maria was floating up in space as she kicked and screamed, "Help me! Help me!" Every time she kicked and screamed, she went up.

Matt knew there were two things he could do to help. He could call the Rescue Squad and have them come with a rope for Maria, or he could try to get Maria down alone. Matt didn't know what to do. He was about to call the Rescue Squad when he saw his Uncle Lucky coming down the street.

"Uncle Lucky," screamed Matt. "Help!"

"Matt, my boy, what can I do for you?"
Then Uncle Lucky looked up. There was
Maria high in the air.

"What were you doing, Maria? Were you
jumping rope?" He began to laugh. "Wait
there, Maria. Don't go away."

Uncle Lucky turned to Matt. "We'd better
get Maria down right now. If I had a rope, I
could do it."

Then Uncle Lucky saw the bowling ball.

"Why is this here?" he asked Matt, as he
went to pick up the ball by its handle. You
know by now that Maria needed to hold the
bowling ball to keep her down."

"Yes, I do know," said Matt. "We were
rushing to bowling class because we were
late. I wanted to help Maria glide a little
faster so I was holding it for her. I did not
remember how important it was for Maria to
hold the ball."

"Matt, you always talk about going to
the Earth. If you want to travel in space,

you will have to remember these little things
as well as the big things," said Uncle Lucky.

"I will, Uncle Lucky," said Matt. "I will."

"Now, Maria," said Uncle Lucky, "please
listen to me."

Uncle Lucky pushed the ball to Maria,
with the handle that was on top.

"When the handle comes to you," said Uncle Lucky, "reach for the handle slowly."

Uncle Lucky let go, and the ball began to move and turn slowly through space. But before it got to Maria, it began to float back down again to Uncle Lucky.

"Oh, no," said Matt. "It's too late."

"We'd better try to help Maria again," said Uncle Lucky.

Then Uncle Lucky pushed the ball a second time. This time it went right to Maria. Then she got a good hold of it. This time, she began to float slowly down to Uncle Lucky and Matt.

When Maria was down she said, "It is good to be back on the ground again. Why did I fly up like that, Uncle Lucky?"

"It was velocipitis. When you let go of the bowling ball, you went up. Each time you began to come down, you kicked and screamed, and you pushed yourself back up again."

"I will remember next time," said Maria.

"You are so little, Maria. You have so much to learn," said Matt.

"And I am lucky because I have you to help me," Maria laughed.

Questions

Read and think.
1. Where did Matt and Maria live?
2. Why is it so hard to walk on the moon?
3. Why did Maria go up in the air?
4. How did Uncle Lucky help Maria?

UNIT TWO
LEVEL 9

TRAILS
TO
TRAVEL

PREPARING FOR READING

Learning Vocabulary

Listen for the vowel.

bird

germs   here   hurt   car
work   sparks   third   hurray

Read the sentences.

1. I had the worst seat in the car, but I didn't care.
2. We were off to the ocean on a seven day trip.
3. I was happy that we were not going too far on the highway.

worst   seat   seven
far   highway

Developing Background

Read and talk.

A Car Trip

Car trips can be fun, but if you are going far and have to sit for a long time, you can get very tired in a car seat. What can you do on a car trip to keep busy? You might keep track of special kinds of cars on the highway. You might make pictures of a special bridge or buildings you see. You might read what the streets and roads are called. You might make a map or read one. The family in the story "Stuck in Traffic" does something special on their car trip. Why was it special?

123

STUCK IN TRAFFIC

BARBARA GREENBERG

Marta, Carlos, and Mother got into the car.

Father was the last one to take his seat. It was summer and the family was going away for seven days.

"Turtle Island, here we come!" Carlos called out.

"We will be there at five," said Marta. "I wish it were not so far."

"It is a long ride," said Father, "but we can have a good time. It isn't that far."

As Father drove the car through streets they knew, they saw some friends.

"Have a good time," one friend called to them. "I hope you have good weather."

Mother's friend Susan called out to them, "Stop, please. I was up at seven to pick some apples for you to take on your trip."

"Thank you," Mother said laughing. "We like apples."

They drove on many streets and roads and came to a tollbooth. They made a stop at the tollbooth, and at last were on the highway.

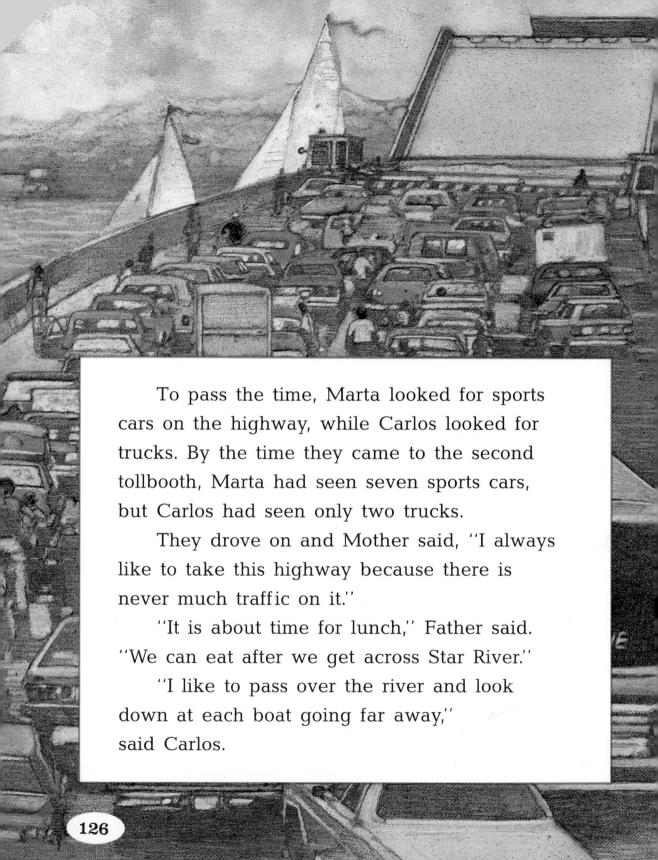

To pass the time, Marta looked for sports cars on the highway, while Carlos looked for trucks. By the time they came to the second tollbooth, Marta had seen seven sports cars, but Carlos had seen only two trucks.

They drove on and Mother said, "I always like to take this highway because there is never much traffic on it."

"It is about time for lunch," Father said. "We can eat after we get across Star River."

"I like to pass over the river and look down at each boat going far away," said Carlos.

But when they came to the river, there was a line of traffic that couldn't move.

"Look, the bridge is up," Carlos said. "It's up so that boat with the sail can pass. Soon it will go down and then we can drive again."

When it didn't go down, Father went to see what was wrong.

He came back and said, "The bridge is stuck for now. The man who works there has called for help. But it will be a while before help comes."

A woman in the car on their right said, "I hope we will not have to be here too long. I'm going to a party that is not very far from here. I have some chicken for the people to have for lunch. This is the worst time for me to get stuck in traffic. I must be there on time."

Soon people got out of their cars and began talking together about the different kinds of highway traffic they had seen on different roads. Some of them said that this was the worst traffic they had been in.

The people spoke about the places they were going to drive to, as soon as the traffic was over, and they could move.

"I'm going to teach an exercise class," a woman said.

"I am going to a country fair where I will show my shell collection," said a boy called Mike.

"I am a shell collector, too," Carlos said.

Mike spoke to Carlos about some of the new shells that he had. Carlos had some of the same shells.

Mike said, "Why don't you come over and have a seat in my car, and I'll show you my shell collection."

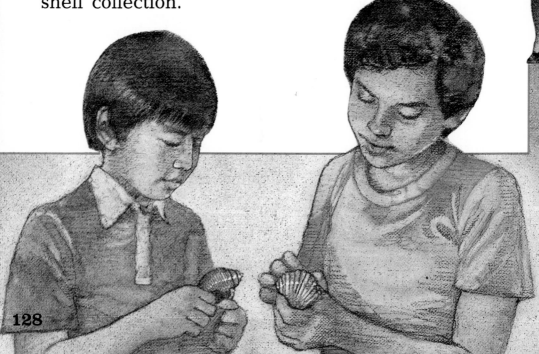

While Carlos was at Mike's car, he could hear one woman say, "I don't think I'll get to the party on time. Why don't we make the best of this day? We can have a picnic party right here. Our cars are stuck where they are, but we can go off the road and sit by those trees and eat the chicken."

The boys went over to join the party. They helped pass the food to all those who wanted something to eat.

Mother said, "We have some apples with us. We'll pass them around, too."

Then the exercise teacher said, "We have not moved very much for a long while. It might be useful to do some exercises. Why don't we try some?"

So they did the exercises together, laughing all the time.

"Look!" Carlos called out. "The bridge is going down."

"We can drive again," called Father.

Before they went back to their cars, the people said, "Thank you" to the exercise teacher and to the women for the food.

Mike said to Carlos, "Remember to write to me when you get new shells."

"You write, too," said Carlos.

"I'm so happy that we had to stop at Star River," Marta said, as she went to her seat. "We were stuck in the worst traffic but we had the best time."

"I'm happy I found a new friend," said Carlos. "I hope that Mike can come to see me someday."

The family went on with the trip to Turtle Island. They had many good days on the trip, but the one they liked best to talk about was the day at Star River.

Questions

Read and think.

1. Why did the bridge at Star River go up?
2. Why was there a line of traffic by Star River?
3. What did the people do to pass the time?
4. Why do you think the family liked their day at Star River so much?

PREPARING FOR READING

Learning Vocabulary

Listen for the suffix: ful.

hope + ful = <u>hopeful</u>

To be <u>hopeful</u> is to be full of hope.

play + ful = playful

use + ful = useful

Read the sentences.

1. It is <u>helpful</u> to <u>buckle</u> up when you travel in a car.
2. You may be in <u>danger</u> if you don't buckle up.
3. Some people say the <u>law</u> can't <u>prevent</u> a driver from running into you.

helpful   buckle   danger   law   prevent

132

Developing Background

Read and talk.

A Safe Rider

Are you a safe rider when you go in a car or bus? A safe rider is as important as a safe driver. Safe riders buckle their seat belts. A safe rider in a bus or car doesn't jump up and down or get in the way of the driver. A safe rider doesn't scream or talk too loudly. Can you think of more ways a safe rider can help prevent an accident? There are many things you will learn about safety in the story, "Car Safety."

CAR SAFETY

Susan Alberghini

An airplane is ready to take off. The people listen as the pilot says, "Buckle your seat belts, please." All the people on the plane must put on their seat belts before the plane ride.

The train ride at the country fair is ready to go. The children listen and hear, "Buckle your seat belts, please." They must buckle their seat belts before the ride is turned on.

For both these special rides, seat belts are needed for safety. But every day in every city in our country, many people don't use their seat belts for the many rides they take in the family car.

Are these people in danger? Yes!

If people in an accident use seat belts, their lives may not be lost. They may not be hurt. Seat belts are very helpful. They are one of the ways to prevent people from flying about or falling out of a car if there is an accident.

In 1967, our country had a helpful new law that was an important step on the road to traffic safety. The law said that all new cars had to have seat belts. But only some people use their seat belts. Why doesn't everybody use seat belts?

Some people say they can't always remember to "buckle up." Some people say that the seat belts don't feel right. Some people say that they are afraid to use seat belts because they don't want to be stuck in the car in an accident. They want to feel that they can get out of the car very fast if they have to.

To help people remember to use their seat belts, cars now have a sound or a light to warn them to buckle up. For people who say the belts don't feel right, work has been done to improve them and make them feel better. New belts that go across the body now have been made that feel better. For the people who are afraid to use seat belts, we now know that the use of seat belts does prevent people from being hurt in an accident.

In many places across our country, there
is a helpful law which says that small
children must be in a special car seat. Older
children must use the car seat belts.

New York was the first place to pass a
law which says that all people must use
their seat belts.

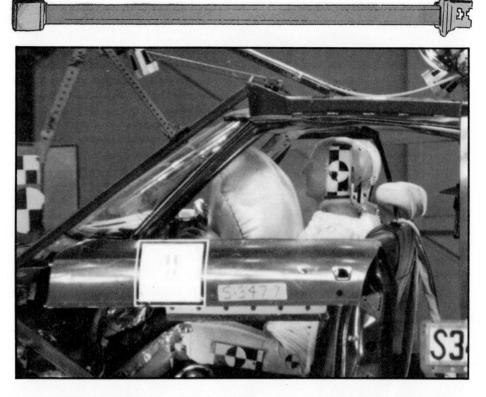

The use of an air bag has helped to improve traffic safety. The air bag was first put into cars in the 1970s. The air bag can be found in the front of the car. It can't be seen by the driver, and the driver does not have to remember to use it.

If there is an accident, the air bag blows up very fast. When it blows up, it looks like a huge bubble. An air bag can help prevent people in the front seat from being hurt. Their lives will not be in danger.

After an accident, the air comes out of the bag so there is no danger that the people will be stuck in the car. The air bag can be very useful. Someday we may have a law in our country that says that every new car must have an air bag in it.

Now you know some important things about car safety. You can think of ways to improve your own safety when you travel. You should always remember to "buckle up."

Questions

Read and think.

1. What does the 1967 law say that all new cars must have?

2. Where is there a law that says all people must use their seat belts?

3. What has been done to help people remember to buckle their seat belts?

4. How does an air bag improve traffic safety?

PREPARING FOR READING

Learning Vocabulary

Listen for the suffix: less.

sleep + less = sleepless

To be <u>sleepless</u> is to be without sleep.

use + less = useless

care + less = careless

Read the sentences.

1. The day before our trip was <u>endless</u>.

2. I <u>just</u> had to <u>pack</u> my bag, and then we were ready to go.

3. The <u>men</u> in the family, my father and brothers, were not going with us.

endless   just   pack   men

Developing Background

Read and talk.

Going On a Trip

What must you do to get ready for a car trip? Read about the different things you might do.

1. Pack your bag, but don't take more than you need.
2. If you like to picnic, you might make a lunch.
3. Get a map and find out what roads you will take.
4. Look to see if the car has gas and oil in it.

"Just Us Women" is a story about a car trip. Did the people in the story do these things to get ready for their trip?

JUST US WOMEN

Jeannette Caines

Soon we will be ready to travel on the endless highway.

Aunt Martha and I are going to drive to North Carolina in her new car.

Aunt Martha says, "No boys and no men, just us women."

Last night we wrote down all the things we needed to take with us.

Aunt Martha can't always remember all
the things to pack, so I help her.

She has a special road map and directions
to help her find her way between places.

Last year she didn't remember to pack the
map or the lunch. She left them both in her
yellow bag in the house.

I was the one to pack the map and our lunch
in a bag this time. I put in chicken, milk, and
a game to play between stops.

We are going to put the food in a lunch box
just as Aunt Martha did when she was a little girl.

We'll stop at every store by the road to
get the things we like and no one will say,
"We can't stop because we have to make it

there before night," or "No! We are not going to stop again!"

If the rain comes, we'll get out of the car and walk.

We'll say we walked in the rain in New Jersey or Pennsylvania.

Last year we walked in Delaware and Maryland.

We'll walk down endless back roads, talk to the men and women on each farm, and drink milk from dairy cows.

If the apples are fresh, we just might get some and eat them from Virginia to North Carolina.

We'll stop and take endless pictures in front of each museum and in front of all the important buildings. When our chicken runs out, we'll stop for eggs.

We'll turn the day around and have our eggs at night.

When we get there, they will all say, "Where have you been all this time?"

We'll just say to them that we had so much girl talk to do between the two of us.

No boys and no men—just us women.

Questions

Read and think.

1. Where did the two women drive?
2. What didn't Aunt Martha remember to pack last year?
3. What did the two women do when it was raining?
4. Why did Aunt Martha want just women to go on this trip?

PREPARING FOR READING

Learning Vocabulary

Listen for the suffix: less.

care + less = careless

To be <u>careless</u> is to be without care.

air + less = airless

noise + less = noiseless

Read the sentences.

1. It looked <u>hopeless</u> when the circus train was stuck in the snow.
2. We were <u>stranded</u> in <u>eight</u> feet of cold, <u>white</u> snow.
3. There wasn't <u>any</u> way for people to <u>climb</u> up the mountains to get us out.

hopeless   stranded   eight   white
any   climb

Developing Background
Read and talk.

Pack Up the Circus

The circus is coming! Every year the circus goes around the country. Everything in the circus goes from city to city by truck or train. When a circus has its own tent, called a Big Top, circus people have to pack it for travel, too. Today, a circus may not have its own tent, but animals, people and many more things must go into trucks or train cars. "The Circus Train" is a story about a trip on a circus train that Grandpa went on when he was a boy.

THE CIRCUS TRAIN

CAROL CARRICK

"It's hopeless," said Jennifer. "I'll never learn to balance." Grandfather and Jennifer were returning from skating in the park.

"I remember a time when I said things were hopeless," said Grandfather. "I was eight, too. We were stranded in the mountains. Did you know I was with the circus when I was a boy?"

"No," said Jennifer.

"We had to live on a train. In a circus family, everybody does something. My mother was one of the horse riders. My father had to train and take care of the elephants. I helped him. We had to feed and water all eight of the elephants before each show. My best friend was Chuckie.

He'd put on his funny red and white paint an hour before the show. Sometimes he put some on me, too. We were there to say hello to the people and make them laugh when they came in.

"I can remember a time when I got to ride on the elephant's back in the circus show. It's pretty high climbing up there, and you have to hold yourself on with your legs. Everybody likes elephants. They always stop the show when they walk in their line."

"Please, go on with the story," said Jennifer. "How did you get stranded?"

"In the spring we traveled all over the country," said Grandfather. "I couldn't go to school every day because we moved around so much, but I did work for school each night.

"The circus traveled from city to city by train. It had to go right after the last show. When people came out of the big top after the last show, they found that the rest of the circus was missing. It had been moved by truck to the train station."

"But Grandfather, how did you get stranded?" asked Jennifer.

"I'm coming to that," said Grandfather.

"The spring I was eight, the circus was returning from a trip west. Our train began to climb through mountains. The mountains were under a blanket of snow. That night, the rain came with thunder and lightning. Many of the circus people were sleeping, but my father and I were busy with the animals. Any storm scared the elephants. The trick was to talk to them and pet them so they didn't feel afraid.

"What we didn't know was that the rain had melted some of the snow on top of the mountains. The snow began to move down the mountains very fast. We could hear the sound, but from the railroad car we couldn't see the white cloud that was rushing at us. It was a snow slide!

"The snow came roaring across the track in front of the train, sweeping the first eight cars with it. I remember the sound of screaming people and animals.

"My father had to stay with the animals, but I went to find my mother. People were running from car to car. My friend Chuckie was climbing out of the snow. He was all white, like a live snowman.

"I saw a man help my mother climb out of a car that had turned over. We went to find Father to show him that Mother was all right.

" 'We must move the train,' said Mother. 'Some of the people are hurt and need help right away.' "

"Some of the cars were under five feet of snow," Grandfather went on. "We were all in danger. The train was stuck and at any time the snow might slide again. We didn't have any power. It looked hopeless.

"The temperature was going down, and our radio didn't work. We were stranded with no hope of returning to the last station.

" 'It's hopeless,' I said to my father.

" 'No, it's not hopeless. There is something we can try,' said Father. 'We must use the elephants.'

"With Chuckie's help, Father walked the elephants out of their cars. As soon as the elephants were free, a boy screamed.

" 'A lion is out! Run!' he called.

"I saw the lion leap at my mother. She screamed and began to run. All at once she was in the air. One of the elephants had put her out of reach, high up on his back. Mother was not hurt.

"Elephants are special animals. They may be afraid of the thunder and lightning, but they are not scared by a lion.

"The men soon got a rope around the lion and had him climb back into his railroad car. Then my father had the elephants put their weight on the cars that were free. Slowly, slowly, they pushed them back to the station and to safety."

"Boy!" said Jennifer. "That was some story! You must have been proud of your father."

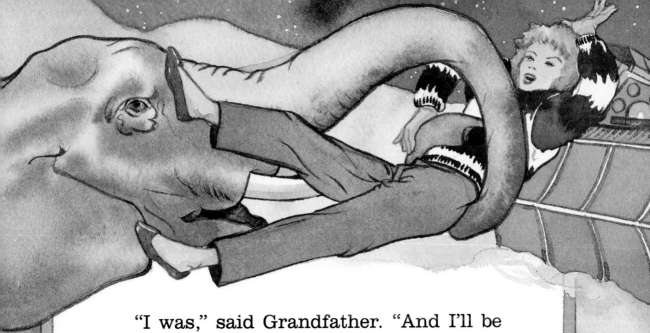

"I was," said Grandfather. "And I'll be proud of you next time we go skating. Remember Jennifer . . . we never say *hopeless* in this family!"

Questions

Read and think.

1. Why was the circus train stranded in the mountains?
2. How did one of the elephants prevent mother from being hurt by a lion?
3. How did the train get back to the station?
4. Why did Grandpa tell Jennifer the story about the circus train?

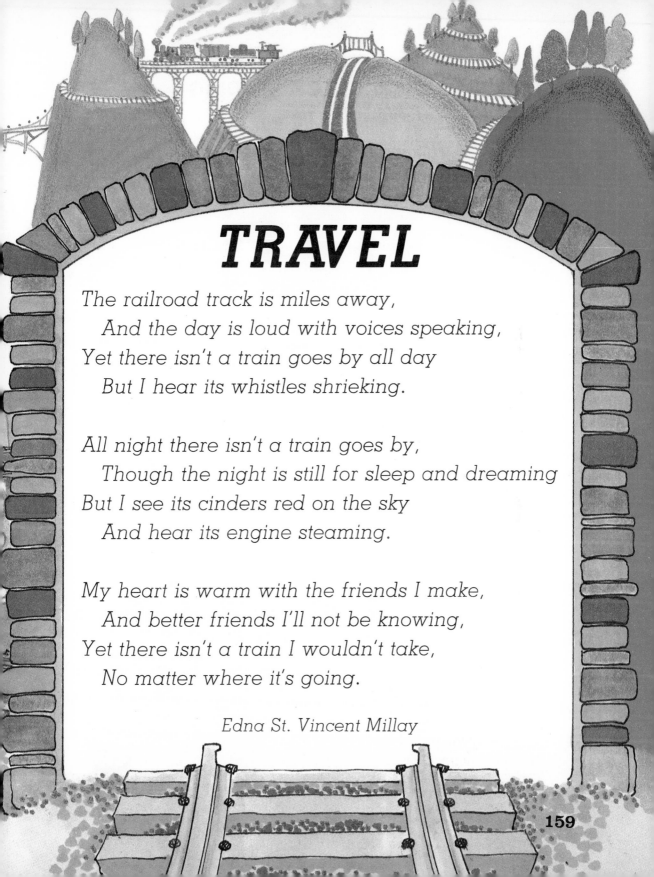

TRAVEL

The railroad track is miles away,
    And the day is loud with voices speaking,
Yet there isn't a train goes by all day
    But I hear its whistles shrieking.

All night there isn't a train goes by,
    Though the night is still for sleep and dreaming
But I see its cinders red on the sky
    And hear its engine steaming.

My heart is warm with the friends I make,
    And better friends I'll not be knowing,
Yet there isn't a train I wouldn't take,
    No matter where it's going.

                Edna St. Vincent Millay

PREPARING FOR READING

Learning Vocabulary

Listen for the vowel.

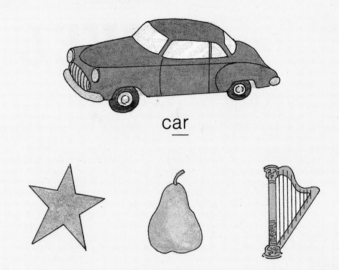

car

Read the sentences.

1. The train <u>starts</u> down the track at a high <u>speed</u>.
2. A <u>passenger</u> on the train doesn't know how many <u>kilometers</u> an hour the train is going.
3. The blue sky <u>above</u> the train and the green <u>hills</u> of the country just fly by.

starts	speed	passenger
kilometers	above	hills

Developing Background

Read and talk.

Trains

Trains have been a way of travel for a long time. Look at the picture and you will see some early trains. Imagine that you were a passenger. The cars were hot in the summer and cold in the winter. The tracks were not always safe, so the train might stop at any time. The train could burn coal, so people had to look out for flying sparks. One of the good things was that the train was faster than a horse or a stagecoach. Today there are new kinds of trains for passenger travel. Read about them in "High-Speed Trains."

HIGH-SPEED TRAINS

CYNTHIA ROTHMAN

People have always wanted to travel from place to place in fast ways. At one time, they traveled by horse, and later they traveled by train.

Today, many people travel by car and airplane each day. But millions of people use trains to go to and from work, and from city to city.

At 7:00 A.M., as the day starts in Tokyo, Japan, a special train brings people into the city. The train is a high-speed electric passenger train called a "bullet train." Imagine what it might feel like to take a seat on that bullet train as it starts to go at a speed of above 160 kilometers (100 miles) an hour. As they sit, passengers can see people, trees, and buildings pass by in a second.

In 1964, the new train line was opened between Tokyo and Osaka. The high-speed electric bullet train could speed its passengers on the new Shinkansen line at above 200 kilometers (125 miles) an hour. It was run by computers in Tokyo and Osaka. Hills could slow the train. Some tracks were above the land so that the train would not have to go up hills or down hills.

Today there are many trips each day
because many passengers want to travel the
Shinkansen line. Each train has as many as 16
cars. People get places on time when they
travel on this train. And train travel doesn't
use much energy.

Safety is important when you travel on
high-speed trains. Every 10 days, the tracks
must be looked at by people who work for the
line. They look at the track to see if it is
strong. If not, people will improve the track.

Travel on the Shinkansen line is very fast,
but the fastest trains in the world travel
through France.

In 1981, the TGV (Train à Grande Vitesse) went 380 kilometers (237 miles) an hour. That was the fastest train travel time in the world. TGV passenger trains are now the fastest in the world as they speed from Paris to Lyon at 270 kilometers (168 miles) an hour.

As the high-speed electric train starts from Paris, a passenger can take a seat in one of 8 cars. A passenger can sit back for a two-hour ride to Lyon, and have food at his or her seat.

A trip on the TGV can take you to 31 different places in France, and there are 108 trips each day. Soon a new line will be opened so that people can travel from France to two places in Switzerland. High-speed train travel can then take the place of car and airplane travel between these places.

Right now, we do not have bullet trains in the United States. Someday we, too, may travel from city to city at 267 kilometers (167 miles) an hour. Think about going to some far away city. Where might you want to go? How long will it take you to get there?

Questions

Read and think.

1. In which country was the first high-speed train line opened?
2. Why do so many people want to travel on high-speed trains?
3. How fast does the TGV travel?
4. Where might you go if you could travel on the bullet train?

PREPARING FOR READING

Learning Vocabulary

Listen for the suffix: ly.

$$slow + ly = slowly$$

<u>Slowly</u> is in a slow way.

$$sad + ly = sadly$$
$$clear + ly = clearly$$

Read the sentences.

1. The people on the big ship were very <u>friendly</u> to the family.

2. A long time <u>ago</u> people in their family had traveled on a ship to <u>settle</u> in a new country.

3. Their dream was to <u>arrive</u> and start a new home.

friendly   ago   settle   arrive

Developing Background

Read and talk.

Ships

In the story "Hello Edward, It's Me Again," the children travel on a big ocean ship from England to a new home in the United States. A long time ago some people came from England on a small ship, called the *Mayflower*, to settle in America and start new homes, too. Their ship was very small next to the ocean ship in the story. Look at the picture of the *Mayflower* that came to America in 1620 and *The United States II*, a big ocean ship. How are these ships different? Are they the same in any way?

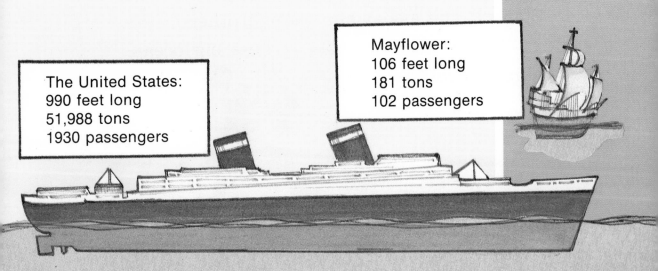

Mayflower:
106 feet long
181 tons
102 passengers

The United States:
990 feet long
51,988 tons
1930 passengers

Hello Edward, It's Me Again

Gibbs Davis

Elizabeth looked at the endless water all around the ship. She was sad because she missed her home in England.

"When will we arrive in the United States?" she asked her older brother.

"Soon," said Michael. "These big ocean ships travel fast."

"We have not been back to the United States for a long time. I can't remember very much about our home there," said Elizabeth. "I was only three when we left."

"Our family pictures help me to remember some things, but it does feel strange going back to people and places that I can't recall," said Michael. "Will Boston look the same to me?" he asked.

"I hope so," said Elizabeth. "Are you a little afraid?"

Michael didn't want to say it, but he was afraid of going to a new place.

That night Michael went to bed early. He had been listening to the roaring ocean for more than an hour, but he couldn't settle down to sleep. It made him unhappy to think he had to start all over again. It wasn't fair. New country, new school, new everything. "A letter to Edward might help," he said.

Hello Edward,

    I am on the ship now. I like the ship, but I will be happy when we arrive in Boston. The first day out I saw a submarine in the ocean. It looked just like the one we made in school.

    Remember the day we let your ant colony out in class? That was so funny!
WRITE TO ME PLEASE.

> Your friend,
> Michael the Fearless

    He began to think about all the fun he had had with Edward and his friends at school. He began to remember the time they went camping in the mountains.

"I don't want to start the year in a new school," said Michael the next day. "I want to go home and see the friendly people I know. I want to go back to England."

"Our home is in the United States now," said his mother. "Our work in England is all done. It is time to make America our home again."

Mother gave a friendly smile to the two sad children.

"As soon as we arrive, I'll show you your new school. We can find a gymnastics club, and you can join right away."

A tiny smile came to Michael, and he said, "Can we join right away?"

"Well, as soon as we get there," said Mother. "Right now, we can all have lunch."

After lunch, Michael went climbing up to the top of the ship with his father.

"Did you know that about 200 years ago people in our family made this same trip?" asked Michael's father.

"Yes," said Michael, "but let me hear the story again."

"Many years ago, people sailed in small ships. They came across the ocean from England to settle in the United States. The United States was a young country. Their lives were hard, but they found a colony of friendly people to live with and help them settle on a farm."

"Do you think they were scared?" Michael asked his father.

"Yes," said his father. "But they had a dream. They were proud to go after it. Their dream was to make a home in a new land."

177

"Now our family is going after the same dream," said Michael.

"That is it, Michael," said his father. "Think about that for now, and we can talk again later."

When Michael came back, Elizabeth asked him for a story. "Please tell me a story now," she said.

"Settle down," said Michael. "I'll tell you a story after I write my letter to Edward."

Hello Edward,

It's me again. We are about to arrive in the States. I walked to the top of the ship today. I spoke with my father. Can you imagine that people in my family made this same trip about 200 years ago? They were proud to go after their dream. It made me think that if they could go to a new country, so can I. When we land, I'm going to scratch *MICHAEL IS HERE* on the first rock I see.

Your friend,
Michael the Fearless

"Please, Michael, a story!" Elizabeth called out.

"Once upon a time," Michael began slowly. "A boy and his sister sailed across the ocean to a new land . . ."

Questions

Read and think.

1. What did Michael do when he couldn't sleep?
2. Why was Michael afraid of going to the United States?
3. What did Michael's mother say that made him feel better?
4. What did Michael's father do that helped him feel better?

PREPARING FOR READING

Learning Vocabulary

Listen for the suffix: ly.

slow + ly = slowly

<u>Slowly</u> is in a slow way.

late + ly = lately

clean + ly = cleanly

Read the sentences.

1. The first colony in America could <u>easily</u> have been the last one.
2. The colony just <u>disappeared</u>.
3. That <u>surprise</u> <u>would</u> stop many people from making a second trip to America.

easily   disappeared   surprise   would

Developing Background

Read and talk.

Making a New Home

A long time ago, people from England came to settle in America. "The Lost Colony" is a story about some of the first people to arrive in the new land. How did people live in that colony? First, they cut trees and made homes. Many people did not know how to farm or fish. Sometimes the Indians were helpful, but they did not want these strange people to take away all their food and land. Can you find out more about how people lived in a colony? Where would you look?

The Lost Colony

Raymond C. Dingledine, Jr.

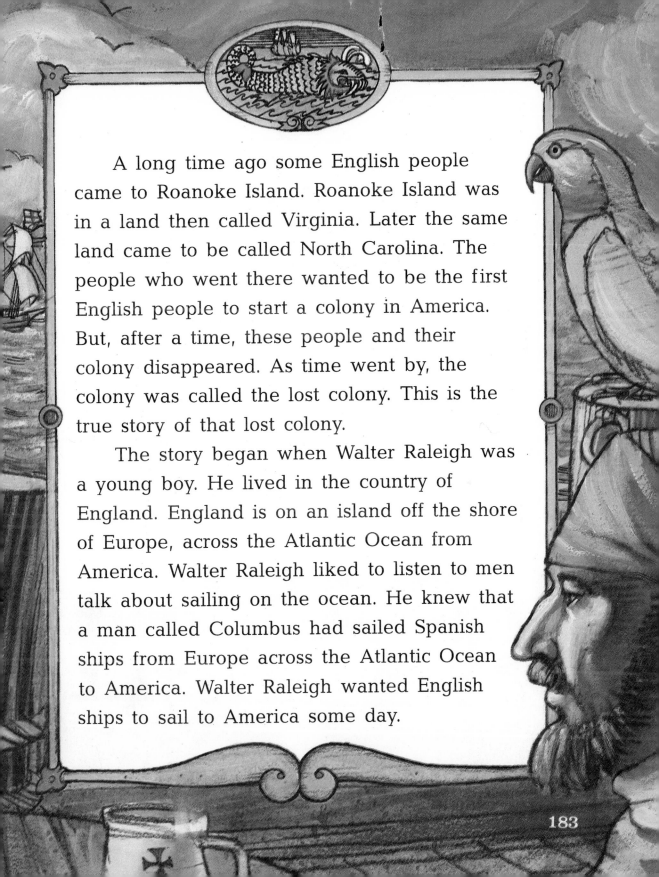

A long time ago some English people came to Roanoke Island. Roanoke Island was in a land then called Virginia. Later the same land came to be called North Carolina. The people who went there wanted to be the first English people to start a colony in America. But, after a time, these people and their colony disappeared. As time went by, the colony was called the lost colony. This is the true story of that lost colony.

The story began when Walter Raleigh was a young boy. He lived in the country of England. England is on an island off the shore of Europe, across the Atlantic Ocean from America. Walter Raleigh liked to listen to men talk about sailing on the ocean. He knew that a man called Columbus had sailed Spanish ships from Europe across the Atlantic Ocean to America. Walter Raleigh wanted English ships to sail to America some day.

Walter Raleigh became a good friend of Queen Elizabeth, the ruler of England. She wanted her country to be strong, and Walter Raleigh wanted to help her. It was his hope that a colony in America would help make England strong.

Walter Raleigh asked some men to sail to America to find a place where he could start an English colony. The men sailed across the ocean to a place called Roanoke Island. There were many fish in the water. There were big trees and many animals and birds on the island. The men became friends with the Indians who lived there.

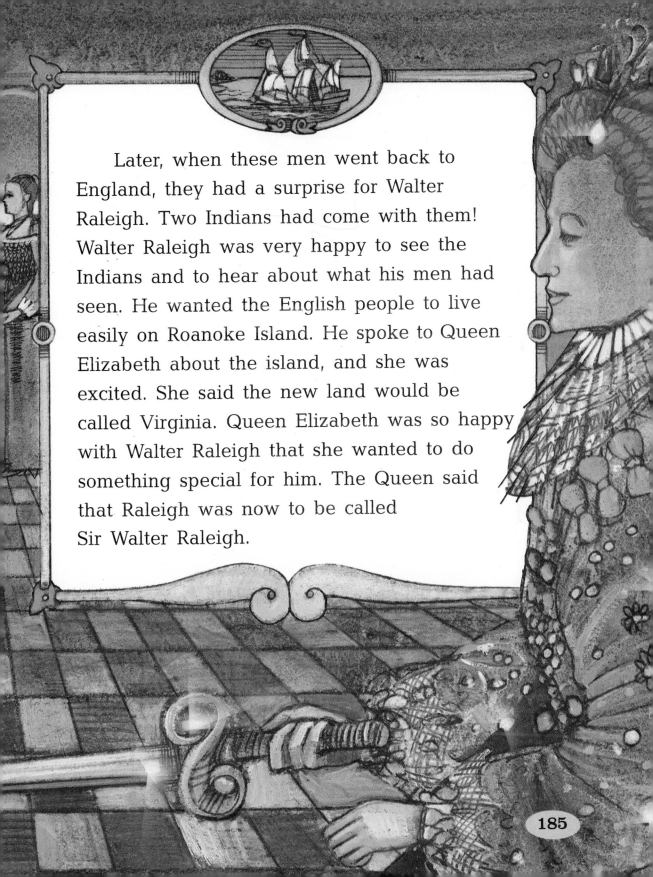

Later, when these men went back to England, they had a surprise for Walter Raleigh. Two Indians had come with them! Walter Raleigh was very happy to see the Indians and to hear about what his men had seen. He wanted the English people to live easily on Roanoke Island. He spoke to Queen Elizabeth about the island, and she was excited. She said the new land would be called Virginia. Queen Elizabeth was so happy with Walter Raleigh that she wanted to do something special for him. The Queen said that Raleigh was now to be called Sir Walter Raleigh.

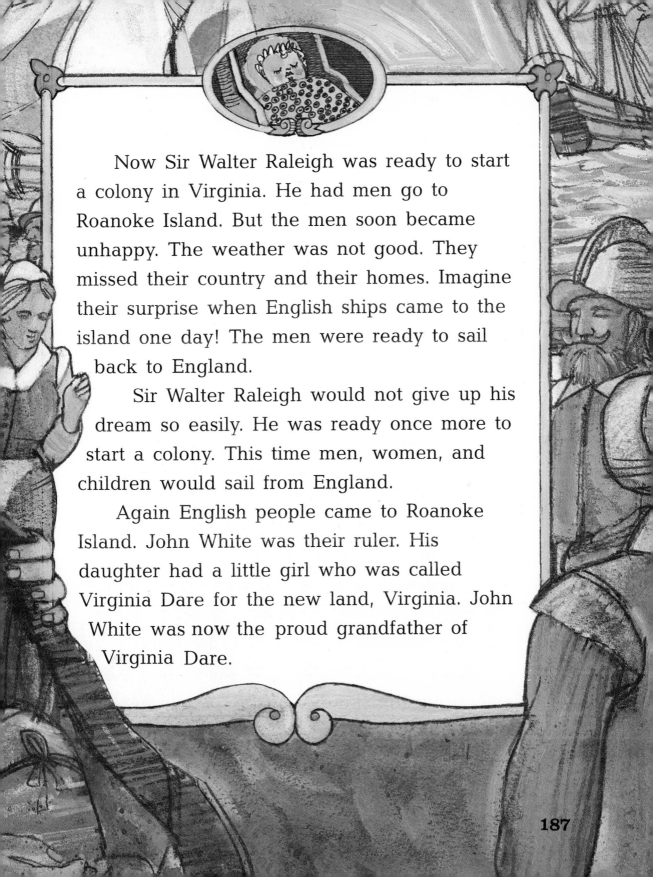

Now Sir Walter Raleigh was ready to start a colony in Virginia. He had men go to Roanoke Island. But the men soon became unhappy. The weather was not good. They missed their country and their homes. Imagine their surprise when English ships came to the island one day! The men were ready to sail back to England.

Sir Walter Raleigh would not give up his dream so easily. He was ready once more to start a colony. This time men, women, and children would sail from England.

Again English people came to Roanoke Island. John White was their ruler. His daughter had a little girl who was called Virginia Dare for the new land, Virginia. John White was now the proud grandfather of Virginia Dare.

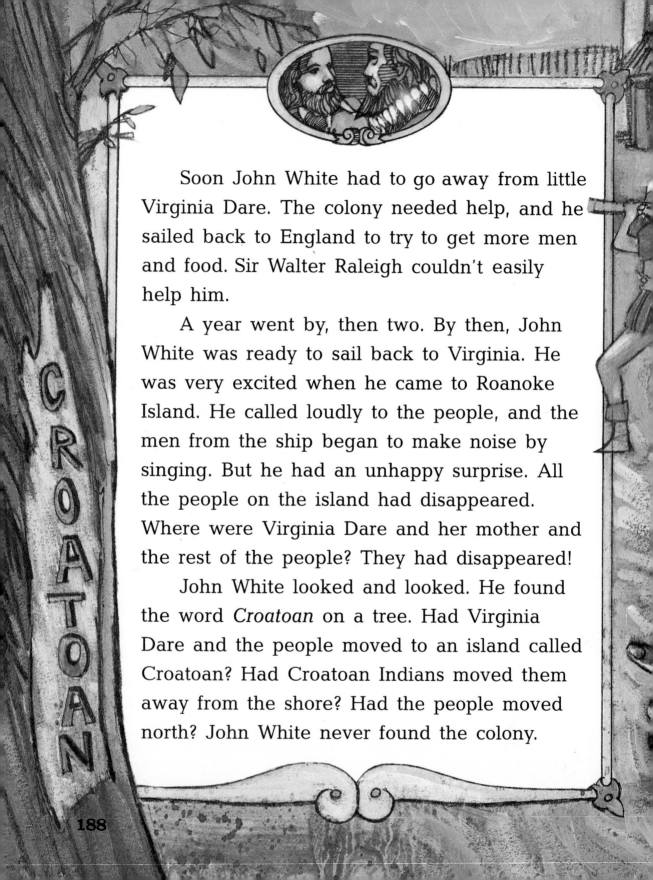

Soon John White had to go away from little Virginia Dare. The colony needed help, and he sailed back to England to try to get more men and food. Sir Walter Raleigh couldn't easily help him.

A year went by, then two. By then, John White was ready to sail back to Virginia. He was very excited when he came to Roanoke Island. He called loudly to the people, and the men from the ship began to make noise by singing. But he had an unhappy surprise. All the people on the island had disappeared. Where were Virginia Dare and her mother and the rest of the people? They had disappeared!

John White looked and looked. He found the word *Croatoan* on a tree. Had Virginia Dare and the people moved to an island called Croatoan? Had Croatoan Indians moved them away from the shore? Had the people moved north? John White never found the colony.

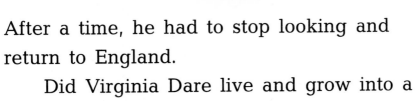

After a time, he had to stop looking and return to England.

Did Virginia Dare live and grow into a woman? We still do not know. The lost colony of Roanoke Island is a true mystery story. But we remember those English people today. We remember Sir Walter Raleigh with a city called Raleigh in North Carolina.

Questions

Read and think.

1. What did Sir Walter Raleigh want to do to help make England strong?
2. Who was John White?
3. Why did John White go back to England?
4. What did John White find when he came back to Roanoke Island?

PREPARING FOR READING

Learning Vocabulary

Listen for the vowel.

car

Read the sentences.

1. My aunt flew to see me in a large plane.
2. The sound of the engine is beautiful to hear, if you like to be in an airplane as much as I do.
3. When I grow up, I shall have a plane just like my aunt's.

large   engine   shall

Developing Background

Read and talk.

A Model Hobby

Making models is a good hobby. Some people have model trains just like the trains in the picture. Small or big sailing ships make some of the best models. Making models of racing cars or very old cars is a good hobby, too. Some of the models in the picture are only for show, but many of them can run as well as big trains, ships, and cars. In "Just Call Aunt Alice," Max is making a model airplane for a contest. Will Aunt Alice help him or doesn't Max want her help?

JUST CALL AUNT

BY GIBBS DAVIS

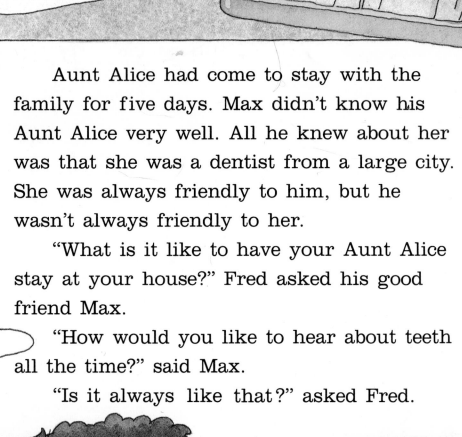

Aunt Alice had come to stay with the family for five days. Max didn't know his Aunt Alice very well. All he knew about her was that she was a dentist from a large city. She was always friendly to him, but he wasn't always friendly to her.

"What is it like to have your Aunt Alice stay at your house?" Fred asked his good friend Max.

"How would you like to hear about teeth all the time?" said Max.

"Is it always like that?" asked Fred.

"Well, my mother said that there is more
to Aunt Alice. She said that I should give
her a chance. She said that I should take
time to get to know her. But I'm too busy
making my new model airplane for the fair,"
said Max.

That night as Max was ready for bed,
Aunt Alice called in, "Did you remember to
brush your teeth?"

"Yes," said Max with a hopeless look.

Then he went back to work on his model
airplane, SPACE CAT. He needed to get the
wings in balance. He wanted the wings to
hold steady when climbing altitude, but he
couldn't get them on right.

"What is wrong?" Aunt Alice asked as
she came in to see him.

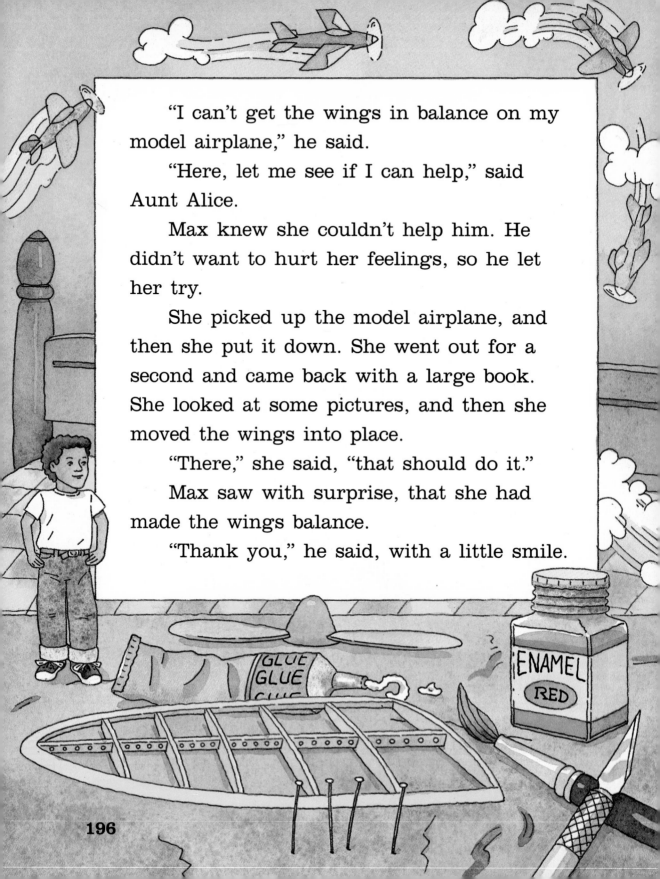

"I can't get the wings in balance on my model airplane," he said.

"Here, let me see if I can help," said Aunt Alice.

Max knew she couldn't help him. He didn't want to hurt her feelings, so he let her try.

She picked up the model airplane, and then she put it down. She went out for a second and came back with a large book. She looked at some pictures, and then she moved the wings into place.

"There," she said, "that should do it."

Max saw with surprise, that she had made the wings balance.

"Thank you," he said, with a little smile.

"Let me listen to the engine," she said. She was listening with care.

"The engine has a good sound," she said. "Your mother said that you would be in the model contest at the fair. You may have yourself a winner here."

"Thank you, Aunt Alice. I hope you are right," said Max.

The next day, Max and Fred went to the fair. Max had SPACE CAT with him, all ready to show to the judges. Max and Fred walked around the fair looking at everything. They walked by Max's plane again, just as the judges were ready to give out first prize.

SPACE CAT

FLYING

BALANCING WINGS

"The first place winner is SPACE CAT!" they called.

Max was jumping with joy as reporters asked for pictures.

"How did you do it?" one asked.

"I made SPACE CAT light and her engine sound," said Max, whose words were like that of a true pilot. "Her wings are in balance so she can hold steady while climbing altitude."

As Max and Fred walked up to the house, Aunt Alice called out to them.

"Did you win? she asked.

"Yes," called Max. "I was the winner. And thank you for all your help."

"Oh," she said. "I was happy to help you. If you need more help, just call Aunt Alice. By the way, did you brush your teeth today?"

"I did brush," said Max. "But, Aunt Alice, I must know. How did you know so much about an airplane? How did you know how to make the wings just right? And why do you have all those books about flying?"

"You will see" is all she said.

At first the boys didn't say a word. Then Max said, "Well, my mother did say there was more to Aunt Alice. She did say that I should give her a chance."

"Will you?" asked Fred.

"I can't, this time," said Max. "Her stay here is over. She has to go at three today."

When it was time for Aunt Alice to go, the family drove her to a large, busy airplane field.

"Why did we stop here?" Max asked.

"This is my airplane," said Aunt Alice. "I went to school to learn how to pilot a plane. And now, Max, shall we?"

"Shall we what?" he asked, with a strange look.

"Shall we go flying? I know that you always dream about flying. Now is your chance," she said.

The airplane soared above the city. Its wings spread out like a large bird. The sound of the engine was like music to Max. He looked at the altitude gauge, as the airplane went up. Aunt Alice called to the air station over her radio.

"Light air traffic," she said. "Flying north at the same altitude."

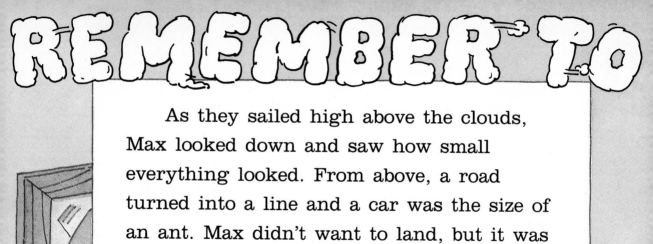

As they sailed high above the clouds, Max looked down and saw how small everything looked. From above, a road turned into a line and a car was the size of an ant. Max didn't want to land, but it was time for Aunt Alice to go.

Before she went off again she called, "Remember to brush!"

Later that day Fred was looking at all the things for his new model airplane spread out on the bed.

"Can't you just help me put it together?" he asked Max.

"Not now," said Max. "I want to finish this letter to Aunt Alice."

BRUSH

Hello Aunt Alice,

I didn't remember to show you my book about flying at night. I will show it to you before we go flying next time.

When are you coming back? I hope it will be soon.

> Your good friend,
> Max

P.S. I brush my teeth every hour now!

Questions

Read and think.

1. How did Aunt Alice help Max?
2. Why did Aunt Alice know so much about flying an airplane?
3. Where did Aunt Alice take Max?
4. Why did Max feel different about Aunt Alice by the time she went home?

PREPARING FOR READING

Learning Vocabulary

Listen for the suffix: ful.

hope + ful = hopeful

To be <u>hopeful</u> is to be full of hope.

thank + ful = thankful

health + ful = healthful

Read the sentences.

1. When you live with danger, you learn to be very <u>careful</u>.
2. In this story, a woman will <u>circle</u> the earth, and a man will fly a high-speed airplane.
3. Both of these people are true <u>heroes</u>.

careful   circle   heroes

Developing Background

Read and talk.

Flying in Space

People have wanted to travel to outer space for a long time. In the United States, NASA runs the space program. Look at the picture from 1961 of the first United States spaceship. Then look at the spaceship in which two men could travel. In 1969, men from the United States flew to the moon. In the story "Two Who Flew," you will read about the first woman to travel on the space shuttle. Then you will read about a man who flew into space in a special Air Force plane.

UNITED STATES

TWO WHO FLEW

RITA M. HOWARD

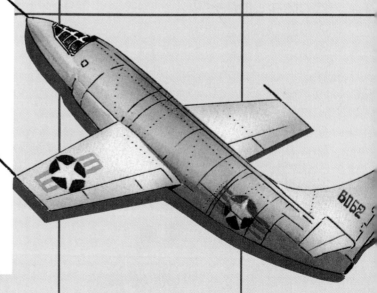

Young and old people can dream about things they would like to do. Sometimes that dream can come true.

You will read about two people whose wishes came true as they soared above the ground. Sally Ride became the first woman to ride in a United States space shuttle. Chuck Yeager was the first man to travel faster than the speed of sound.

The people were excited as they saw the space shuttle climb through the clouds that spring day. It would circle the earth with its team of five people. Only one of the five on the team was a woman. She was Sally Ride, the first woman to travel in outer space for the United States.

As a young girl in Encino, California, Sally had endless energy for sports and for school work, too. To help her learn more about her world, she read as many books as she could.

Sally Ride always liked to be on a team. At that time, many team sports were only played by boys. Because of that, Sally had to play on a team for boys.

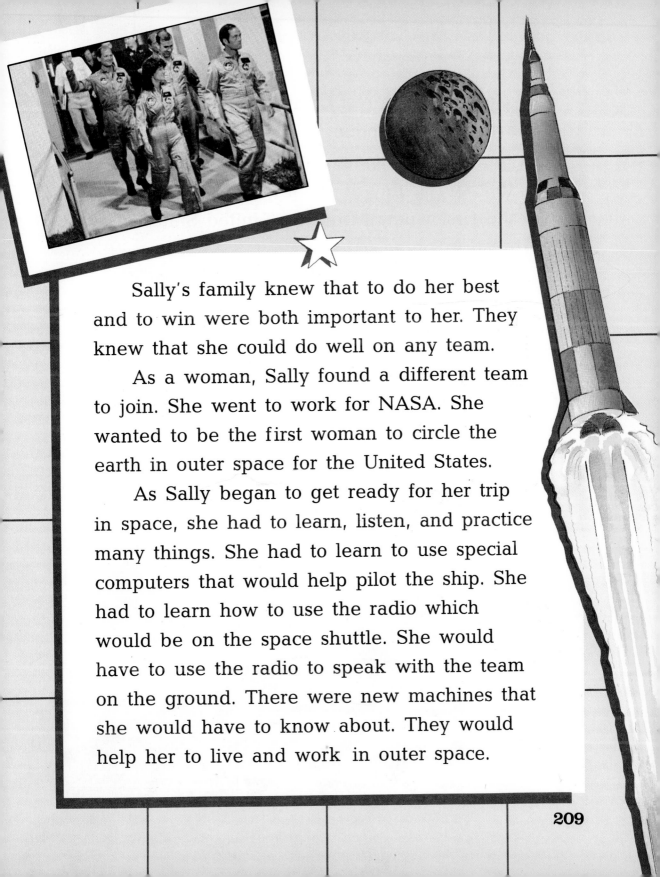

Sally's family knew that to do her best and to win were both important to her. They knew that she could do well on any team.

As a woman, Sally found a different team to join. She went to work for NASA. She wanted to be the first woman to circle the earth in outer space for the United States.

As Sally began to get ready for her trip in space, she had to learn, listen, and practice many things. She had to learn to use special computers that would help pilot the ship. She had to learn how to use the radio which would be on the space shuttle. She would have to use the radio to speak with the team on the ground. There were new machines that she would have to know about. They would help her to live and work in outer space.

Sally and the rest of her team worked with the pilot, Captain Crippen, to get ready for the trip. The space shuttle would take off on that spring day in 1983. Sally Ride would be the first woman from the United States to travel in outer space.

As the ship soared through the clouds, the ground was far away. Soon the ship was making a circle around the earth at a fast speed. For days, Sally and the rest of the team would be busy as the ship went speeding again and again around the earth. As always, Sally was careful about her work. She was proud to be on this special team.

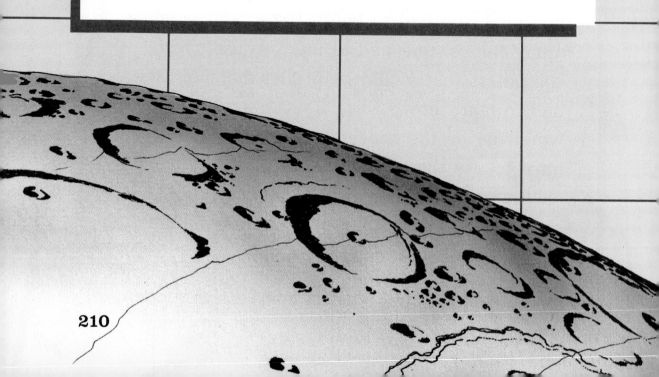

The boy looked up from his game. He could hear a sound in the wind. Soon he saw an airplane speeding across the quiet sky.

"When I'm a man, I shall be a pilot. I will go faster than any pilot," said the boy.

That 14 year old boy was Chuck Yeager. All of Chuck's heroes, the people he liked to read about in books, knew how to fly. Chuck liked to dream about flying.

"When I'm 18," he would say over and over again, "I will join the United States Air Force. I will learn to be a pilot."

That is just what he did.

By the time he was 20, he became as fearless a pilot as any of his heroes. But, he was a careful pilot, too.

The Air Force had a new airplane called the X-1. It was like a rocket. It could go faster than any plane. Sound could travel at the speed of 662 miles an hour. The hope was that the X-1 could fly faster than the speed of sound. The X-1 needed a fearless, but careful, pilot to fly it. The Air Force asked Chuck Yeager if he would pilot the X-1. Could the X-1 fly faster than the speed of sound? Chuck Yeager was ready to try to find out.

Chuck turned the X-1 to the sky. He could see the X-1 had more power than any airplane he had been in before. As he soared above the clouds, Chuck made the X-1 go faster and faster. Flying that airplane was hard work, but he did it easily. He had to keep a careful eye on each gauge that was in front of him. Faster and faster he went. And then, he did it! He was flying faster than the speed of sound!

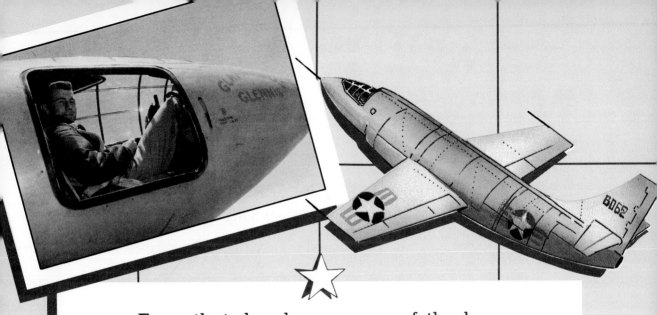

From that day, he was one of the heroes of flying. Now young children would read about Chuck Yeager and dream about flying. They would remember him as the first pilot to fly faster than sound.

Questions

Read and think.
1. What did Sally Ride do that no woman had done before?
2. What did Chuck Yeager do that had never been done before?
3. What do people have to do if they want to do something that has never been done before?
4. What would it be like to travel in space?

WRITING ACTIVITY

WRITE A BIOGRAPHY

Prewrite

"Two Who Flew" is the story of two famous people, Sally Ride and Chuck Yeager. The story has facts about the life of each person. When you write a story about someone's life, it is called a biography. A biography can tell about all of one's life or it can tell a little about the person's life, as in "Two Who Flew."

You are going to write a little biography about a person you know. It can be about someone in your family or a friend. You will need to talk to the person to find out some facts for your biography. Think about these questions. Write the facts in sentences.

1. Who is the person?
2. Where does the person work and live?
3. What does the person like to do for fun?
4. Does the person like to travel? Where?
5. Has the person done something special?
6. Does the person have a special hobby?

Write

1. Read your sentences from page 214.
2. Think about how many paragraphs you will have in your biography. Try to start your biography with a paragraph about the person's hobby or something special he or she can do.
3. Use your sentences from page 214 to write the biography.
4. Use your Glossary for help with spelling.

Revise

Read the biography. You may want the person it is about to read it, too. Did you write just the facts about the person? Did you start with a paragraph that would make someone want to know more about the person? Rewrite what you need to now.

1. Did you indent the first word in each paragraph?
2. Did you use correct capitalization and end punctuation?
3. Did you spell the words correctly?

PREPARING FOR READING

Learning Vocabulary

Listen for the suffix: ly.

quiet + ly = quietly

Quietly is in a quiet way.

free + ly = freely

hour + ly = hourly

Hourly is every hour.

year + ly = yearly

Read the sentences.

1. Suddenly the heavy spaceship was flying through space.

2. The woman could not believe it when she heard the engine start.

suddenly   heavy   believe   heard

Developing Background

Read and talk.

A Special Passenger

May 10, 19___

Dear Irene,

I know you will find what I am going to tell you hard to believe, but we have a special passenger on our trip to Mars. It is Miss Pickerell, and she says that she has been on strange trips before. The captain is very unhappy, but we can't turn back now. Her story would make a good book. It could be called "Miss Pickerell Goes to Mars." I know everybody would want to read about her strange trip. She says she just wants to get home.

Your friend,

Wilbur

Miss Pickerell GOES TO MARS

Ellen MacGregor

Mr. Haggerty was not on the spaceship. He should have been on it, but he wasn't. Miss Pickerell, who should not have been on the spaceship, was on the ship.

The last thing Miss Pickerell remembered was looking at a huge thing in the field with important looking instruments on it. She had seen two men climb up and go in at the top. She got in, too. Now she was in a seat, with a seat belt on.

SHE CLIMBED IN, TOO.

"I must tell the captain," said Mr. Killian. "Mr. Haggerty is not with us, but you are! The captain will not be happy to hear that!"

Miss Pickerell had strange feelings. She didn't know where she was. She began to feel as if she had no weight at all.

"Where am I? Why do I feel so light?" she asked.

"You are on a spaceship. You feel light because we are going through space," she heard Mr. Killian say.

Miss Pickerell knew that she just had to see the captain of this ship. As she opened the buckle of the belt that Mr. Killian had put on her to keep her in place, she suddenly began to float through the air.

"Why, this is fun," said Miss Pickerell. Very soon Miss Pickerell found out how to move around the spaceship. She made her way to where the captain was.

"Who are you and what are you doing on this spaceship?" he asked loudly.

"WHY, THIS IS FUN," SAID MISS PICKERELL.

THIS SPACESHIP IS GOING TO MARS!

"I am Miss Pickerell, and I would like to know how long this ride will last because I need to get my rock collection ready for the fair."

"Miss Pickerell, I will have you know that this is not just a ride. This spaceship is going on an important trip to Mars!" said the captain. "What are you doing here on this spaceship?"

"Did you say Mars?" Miss Pickerell asked. She just couldn't believe it. "I did not know that this spaceship, as you call it, was going to move at all. I don't know why I am here. I do not want to go on a trip right now. I have too much to do on Earth."

"Why don't you try to get some sleep as long as you are here now," said a man called Wilbur.

"I am tired," said Miss Pickerell. But she did not go to sleep right away. First she wanted to think about what she might say to her friends on Earth about her strange trip. It would be a long time before the spaceship would reach Mars.

After a time, Miss Pickerell went to sleep. When she got up from her sleep, she looked through one of the instruments with Wilbur's help.

"Oh," she said, "I see millions of stars, and the sky is black. Is it night?"

"No," said Mr. Killian. "In space it always looks as if it were night."

Miss Pickerell looked through an instrument that was like a telescope. She saw a small red ball far away. She couldn't believe it. Could that be Mars?

Suddenly Miss Pickerell began to believe that she did not need to get home so fast, after all. This was an important trip. She liked the trip now and knew that she could always work on her rock collection later.

Some days later, Miss Pickerell was alone at her seat. She knew something strange was about to take place. Wilbur was very busy with the instruments.

Miss Pickerell tried to sit up, but she couldn't. Her body was heavy. Why did she feel so heavy? She had not had that much food for lunch. Then suddenly she knew why. The spaceship had landed on Mars.

Mr. Killian said, "Now that we have landed, all of us will feel heavy because of the gravity."

Then the men had to get ready to get off their spaceship.

THE SPACESHIP HAD LANDED ON MARS.

"I am ready," said Miss Pickerell.

"I am afraid that I can't let you get off this ship," said the captain. "You do not know the right way to use all of the special things we have for walking around."

The men left. Now Miss Pickerell was alone. Miss Pickerell was unhappy about not going off the ship, but she could talk to the men on a special phone from the spaceship.

"I will look for some rocks for your collection," said Wilbur, with a smile.

It made Miss Pickerell happy to think about how much fun it would be to have rocks from Mars in her collection.

After the men had been off the ship for a while, Miss Pickerell suddenly heard Wilbur calling, "Help me! Help! I can't get my foot out from under this big rock," he said.

Miss Pickerell did not think the captain heard Wilbur because Wilbur called out again and again.

Something must be wrong with the captain's phone. She knew she had to help Wilbur, because he soon would not have much air left. She would put on Mr. Haggerty's things and get off the spaceship. Miss Pickerell remembered what Mr. Killian and Wilbur had done before. She put everything on with care, and then she began to climb down.

WHY WAS MISS PICKERELL THERE?

When she got down to the ground, Miss Pickerell found it was hard to walk. Slowly she made her way over to the captain. Why was Miss Pickerell there?

She said the word *Wilbur* over and over.
Then the captain knew why Miss Pickerell
was there. He knew he had not seen Wilbur
for a while, and he wanted to find him. Soon
he found Wilbur and helped him get his foot
out from under the big rock. Then Miss
Pickerell and the men all went slowly back
to the spaceship.

From that day on, Miss Pickerell was a
very important passenger on the spaceship.
Mr. Killian and Wilbur gave her some of the
best rocks for her collection. Miss Pickerell
would have the best collection at the fair.
The captain said that Miss Pickerell was
special for what she had done. He was now
very happy that she was on the spaceship.

Soon it would be time to go back to the
farm. Miss Pickerell was happy to have seen
Mars, but she was very happy to be going
home again, too.

"Do you think my friends will believe me
when I tell them where my rocks came
from?" she asked.

SHE WAS VERY HAPPY TO GO HOME.

Questions

Read and think.

1. Where was Miss Pickerell sitting?
2. Why did Miss Pickerell feel so light on the spaceship?
3. How did Miss Pickerell feel about being on the spaceship?
4. Why do you think the captain said that Miss Pickerell was special?

Last Laugh

They all laughed when I told them
I wanted to be

A woman in space
Floating so free.

But they won't laugh at me
When they finally see
My feet up on Mars
And my face on TV.

Lee Bennett Hopkins

231

PADDINGTON
TAKES TO THE ROAD

Michael Bond

Paddington Bear lives in England with the Brown family — Mr. and Mrs. Brown, Judy and Jonathan Brown, and the housekeeper, Mrs. Bird. They are spending the summer in a village in France called St. Castille.

Paddington hears of a famous bicycle race called the "Tour de France" that will pass through the village. Paddington was most interested in the idea of anyone being able to win a prize simply by being the fastest person to ride down a hill on a bicycle.

Paddington felt sure that with a bright and shiny tricycle he would stand a very good chance indeed of winning a prize in the "Tour de France" cycle race.

The Browns were wakened earlier than usual the next morning by the comings and goings in the square outside the hotel. There was an air of great excitement, and every few minutes a loud-speaker van passed by and addressed the crowd which had collected on the pavement round the square and at the side of the hill leading out of the village.

The Browns had arranged to meet on the balcony outside Paddington's room from where there was a fine view of the hill, but to their surprise when they gathered there Paddington himself was nowhere to be seen.

"I do hope he won't be long," said Mrs. Brown. "He'll be most upset if he misses any of it."

"I wonder where on earth he can have got to?" said Mr. Brown. "I haven't seen him since breakfast."

"H'mm!" said Mrs. Bird, as she looked around the room. "I have my suspicions."

Mrs. Bird's sharp eyes had already noticed the remains of some hastily removed tire tracks on the floor. They went round the room several times and then out through the door before finally disappearing in the direction of some stairs which led to the back door of the hotel.

Fortunately for Paddington, before Mrs. Bird had time to say any more there was a burst of clapping from the crowd on the pavement below, and so the subject was forgotten as the Browns looked over the balcony to see what was happening.

"How very odd," said Mrs. Brown, as the clapping grew louder and several people cheered. "They seem to be pointing at us."

The Browns became more and more mystified as they waved back at the crowd.

"I wonder what they mean by 'Vive le Bear'?" said Mr. Brown. "It can't be anything to do with Paddington—he isn't here."

"Goodness only knows," said Mrs. Brown. "I suppose we shall just have to wait and see."

Had they but known, the Browns weren't the only ones to wonder what was going on at that moment, but fortunately for their peace of mind there were several streets and a large number of houses between them and the cause of all the excitement.

At the other end of the village Paddington was even more puzzled at the way things were going. In fact, the more he tried to think about the matter the more confused he became.

One moment he had been sitting quietly on his tricycle in a side street, peering round the corner every now and then and checking the marmalade sandwiches in the basket on his handlebars as he waited for the race to appear.

The next moment, as the first of the riders came in sight and he pedaled out to join them, everything seemed to go wrong at once.

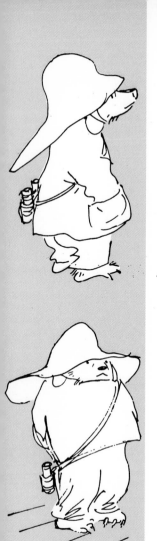

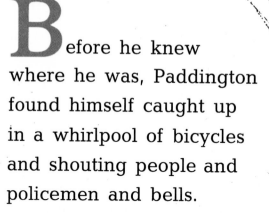

Before he knew where he was, Paddington found himself caught up in a whirlpool of bicycles and shouting people and policemen and bells.

He pedaled as hard as he could and raised his hat to several of the other cyclists, but the harder he pedaled and the more he raised his hat the louder they shouted and waved back at him, and by then it was much too late to change his mind and turn back even if he'd tried.

Everywhere he looked there were bicycles and men in shorts and striped shirts. There were bicycles in front of him. There were bicycles to the left and bicycles to the right of him. Paddington was much too busy pedaling for dear life to look back, but he was sure there were bicycles behind him as well because he could hear heavy breathing and the sound of bells ringing.

In the excitement someone handed him a bottle of milk as he went past, and in trying to take the bottle with one paw and raise his hat with the other, Paddington had to let go of the handlebars. He went twice round a statue in the middle of the street before joining the stream of cyclists as they swept round a corner on to a road leading out of the village.

Luckily the road was uphill and most of the other cyclists were tired after their long ride, so that by standing on the pedals and jumping up and down as fast as he could he was able to keep up with them.

It was as they reached the top of the hill and rounded another corner leading back down into the village that things suddenly took a decided turn for the worse. Just as he was about to sit back on the saddle and have a rest while he got his second wind, Paddington found to his surprise that without even having to turn the pedals he was beginning to gather speed.

In fact he hardly had time to wave to the crowd before he found himself starting to overtake the riders in front. He passed one, then another, and then a whole bunch. The cyclists looked quite startled as Paddington flashed by, and all the time the cheering from the spectators on the side of the road grew louder. Quite a number recognized him, and they called out words of encouragement, but by then Paddington was much too worried to notice.

He tried pulling as hard as he could on the brake lever but nothing happened. In fact if anything he seemed to go faster than ever, and he began to wish he hadn't used quite so much oil on the moving parts when he'd cleaned them.

By then the pedals were going round so fast that he sat back on the saddle and hurriedly lifted up his feet in case his legs fell off.

It was as he gave the brake lever an extra hard pull that he had his second big shock of the day, for it suddenly came away in his paw. Paddington rang his bell frantically and waved the lever as he overtook the last of the riders in front.

"Apply your brakes, Monsieur le Bear!" yelled a man in English as he recognized the Union Jack on Paddington's handlebars.

"I don't think I can," cried Paddington, looking most upset as he shot past. "My lever's come off in my paw by mistake, and I think I've left some of the bits in my box at the hotel!"

Paddington clung to the handlebars of his tricycle as he hurtled on down the hill towards the village square. All the villagers were most excited when they saw who was in the lead, and a great cheer went up as he came into view, but as he lifted the brim of his hat and peered out anxiously, all Paddington could make out was a sea of white faces and a blurred picture of some buildings looming up ahead which he didn't like the look of at all.

But if Paddington was worried the Browns were even more alarmed.

"Good heavens!" exclaimed Mr. Brown. "It's Paddington!"

"He's heading straight for Monsieur Dupont's shop," cried Mrs. Brown.

"I can't watch," said Mrs. Bird.

"Why on earth doesn't he put his brakes on?" exlaimed Mr. Brown.

"Crickey!" exclaimed Jonathan. "He can't! His brake lever's come off!"

It was Monsieur Dupont himself who saved Paddington. Right at the very last moment his voice rose above the roar of the crowd.

"This way, Monsieur le Bear," he cried, as he flung open the big double gates at the side of his shop. "This way!"

And before the astonished gaze of the onlookers, Paddington shot through them and disappeared from view.

As the rest of the cyclists sped past unheeded, the crowd surged forward and gathered round Monsieur Dupont's shop. The Browns only just managed to force their way through to the front before a gasp went up from everyone as a small white figure came into view through the doors.

Even Paddington looked very worried when he saw his reflection in Monsieur Dupont's window, and he pinched himself several times to make sure he was all right before raising his hat to the crowd, revealing a small round patch of brown fur.

"I'm not a ghost," he exclaimed. "I think I must have landed on one of Mr. Dupont's sacks of flour!"

And as the crowd gathered round Paddington to shake him by the paw, Monsieur Dupont echoed the feelings of them all.

"We of St. Castille," he cried, "shall remember for many years to come the day the 'Tour de France' passed through our village."

There was a great deal of celebrating in the village that evening, and everyone applauded when the mayor announced that he was giving Paddington a special prize, with as many buns as he could manage into the bargain.

"Not for the fastest rider through the village," he said, amid cheers and laughter, "but certainly for the fastest down the hill!"

Glossary

This glossary can help you to pronounce and find out the meanings of words in this book that you may not know.

The words are listed in alphabetical order. Guide words at the top of each page tell you the first and last words on the page.

Each word is divided into syllables. The way to pronounce each word is given next. You can understand the pronunciation respelling by using the key on the next page. A shorter key appears at the bottom of every other page.

When a word has more than one syllable, a dark accent mark (') shows which syllable is stressed. In some words, a light accent mark (') shows which syllable has a less heavy stress.

The following abbreviations are used in this glossary:

n. noun   *v.* verb   *adj.* adjective   *adv.* adverb
pl. plural

The glossary entries were adapted from the Macmillan *Beginning Dictionary·*

PRONUNCIATION KEY

Vowel Sounds

/a/ b**a**t

/ā/ c**a**ke, r**ai**n, d**ay**

/ä/ f**a**ther

/är/ c**ar**

/ār/ d**are**, h**air**

/e/ h**e**n, br**ea**d

/ē/ m**e**, m**ea**t, bab**y**, bel**ie**ve

/ėr/ t**er**m, f**ir**st, w**or**m, t**ur**n

/i/ b**i**b

/ī/ k**i**te, fl**y**, p**ie**, l**igh**t

/ir/ cl**ear**, ch**eer**, h**ere**

/o/ t**o**p, w**a**tch

/ō/ r**o**pe, s**oa**p, s**o**, sn**ow**

/ô/ s**aw**, s**o**ng, **au**to

/oi/ c**oi**n, b**oy**

/ôr/ f**or**k, **ore**, **oar**

/ou/ **ou**t, c**ow**

/u/ s**u**n, s**o**n, t**ou**ch

/u/ b**oo**k, p**u**ll, c**ou**ld

/ü/ m**oo**n

/ū/ c**u**te, f**ew**, m**u**sic

/ə/ **a**bout, tak**e**n, penc**i**l, apr**o**n, helpf**u**l

/ər/ lett**er**, doll**ar**, doct**or**

Consonant Sounds

/b/ **b**ear

/d/ **d**og

/f/ **f**ish, **ph**one

/g/ **g**oat

/h/ **h**ouse, **wh**o

/j/ **j**ar, **g**em, fu**dge**

/k/ **c**ar, **k**ey

/l/ **l**amb

/m/ **m**ap

/n/ **n**est, **kn**ow

/p/ **p**ig

/r/ **r**ug, **wr**ong

/s/ **c**ity, **s**eal

/t/ **t**iger

/v/ **v**an

/w/ **w**agon

/y/ **y**o-**y**o

/z/ **z**oo, egg**s**

/ch/ **ch**ain, ma**tch**

/sh/ **sh**ow

/th/ **th**in

/<u>th</u>/ **<u>th</u>**ose

/hw/ **wh**ere

/ng/ so**ng**

A

a · bove (ə buv′) *prep.* over or higher than

ac · ci · dent (ak′ sə dənt) *n.* **1.** something that happens for no apparent reason and is not expected. **2.** an unhappy event that is not expected.

a · fraid (ə frād′) *adj.* feeling fear; frightened.

a · go (ə gō′) *adj.* before now; past.

air · bag (ār′ bag′) a bag that fills with air when there is a car accident, to prevent people from getting hurt.

air force (ār′ fôrs′) the branch of a country's army in charge of aircraft and air warfare.

al · ti · tude (al′ tə tüd′ *or* al′ tə tūd′) *n.* the height that something is above the ground or above sea level.

A · mer · i · ca (ə mār′ i kə) *n.* **1.** The United States. **2.** North America or South America.

an · y (en′ ē) *adj.* **1.** every. **2.** one, no matter which; some.

ar · rive (ə rīv′) *v.* **ar · rived, ar · riv · ing.** to come to a place.

At · lan · tic O · cean (at lan′tik ō′ shən) *n.* the large body of water separating Europe and Africa from North America and South America

B

be · lieve (bi lēv′) *v.* **be · lieved, be · liev · ing.** to have trust or faith in the truth of .

be · tween (bi twēn′) *prep.* in the space, time, or range separating.

Big Dip · per (big′ dip′ ər) a group of stars in the northern sky that are in the shape of a dipper, a cup with a long handle. *See also,* **Little Dipper.**

bil · lion (bil′ yən) *n.* a thousand millions.

Bos · ton (bôs′ tən) *n.* the capital of Massachusetts, in the eastern part of the state.

bounce (bouns) *v.* **bounced, bounc · ing.** to spring back from a surface; rebound.

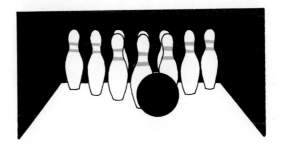

bowl · ing (bō′ ling) *n.* a game played by rolling a heavy ball down an alley to knock over wooden pins at the far end.

245

bridge (brij) *n.* anything built across a river, road, or railroad track so that people can get from one side to the other.

bright · ly (brīt′ lē) *adv.* in a bright manner; with much light.

buck · le (buk′ əl) *v.* **buck · led, buck · ling.** to fasten with a buckle.

bul · let (bùl′ it) *n.* A small piece of rounded or pointed metal.

burn (bėrn) *v.* **1.** to set on fire; be on fire. **2.** to use for light or heat.

C

care · ful (kār′ fəl) *adj.* paying close attention; watchful.

chief (chēf) *n.* a person who is highest in rank or power; leader of a group.

cir · cle (sėr′ kəl) *n.* a closed curved line. *v.* **cir · cled, cir · cling.** to make a circle around.

clear · ly (klir′ lē) *adv.* in a clear manner; plainly, distinctly.

climb (klīm) *v.* to move or go upward.

coal (kōl) *n.* a black mineral that is used as a fuel.

col · lec · tor (kə lek′ tər) *n.* anything that collects, or gathers something together.

col · o · ny (kol′ ə nē) *n., pl.* **col · o · nies. 1.** a group of people who leave their own country and settle in another land. **2.** a group of animals or plants of the same kind that live together.

Co · lum · bus (kə lum′ bəs) *n.* **Christopher.** 1451?–1506, the Italian explorer who discovered America and other lands.

Crete (krēt) *n.* a Greek island in the eastern Mediterranean Sea.

Cro · a · to · an (krō′ ə tō′ ən) *n.* **1.** an island off the coast of North Carolina. **2.** an Indian tribe formerly inhabiting the coastal region of North Carolina.

D

dan · ger (dān′ jər) *n.* the chance that something bad or harmful may happen.

Dare, Vir · gin · ia (dãr′, vėr jin′ yə) 1587–?, the first child of English parents born in America.

Del · a · ware (del′ ə wãr′) *n.* a state in the eastern United States.

di · rec · tion (di rek′ shən *or* dī rek′ shən) *n.* **1.** the line or course along which something moves, faces, or lies. **2.** *also* **directions,** an order or instructions on how to do something or how to act.

dis · ap · pear (dis′ ə pir′) *v.* **1.** to go out of sight; vanish. **2.** to pass away; end.

Dor · ches · ter Coun · ty, Mar · y · land (dôr′ ches′ tər coun′ tē, mãr′ə lənd) *n.* a county in east central Maryland.

E

ear · ly (ėr′ lē) *adv.* before the customary or expected time.

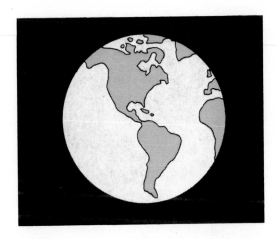

earth (ėrth) *n.* the planet that we live on.

eas · i · ly (ē′ zə lē) *adv.* without trying hard; without difficulty or discomfort.

east (ēst) *n.* the direction you face when watching the sun rise. *adj.* **1.** toward or in the east. **2.** coming from the east.

e · clipse (i klips′) *n.* a darkening or hiding of the sun or the moon.

eight (āt) *adj.* numbering one more than seven.

e · lec · tric (i lek′ trik) *adj.* having to do with electricity; run or produced by electricity.

---

a b**a**t, ā c**a**ke, ä f**a**ther, ãr c**a**r, ãr d**a**re; e h**e**n, ē m**e**, ėr t**e**rm; i b**i**b, ī k**i**te, ir cl**ea**r; o t**o**p, ō r**o**pe, ô s**a**w, oi c**oi**n, ôr f**o**rk, ou **ou**t; u s**u**n, u̇ b**oo**k, ü m**oo**n, ū c**u**te; ə **a**bout, tak**e**n

En · ci · no, Cal · i · for · nia (en sē′ nō, kal′ə fôrn ′yə) a city in southern California.

end · less (end′ lis) *adj.* having no limit or end.

en · er · gy (en′ ər jē) *n., pl.* **en · er · gies.** the capacity for doing work.

en · gine (en′ jin) *n.* a machine that uses energy to run other machines.

Eu · rope (ur ′əp) *n.* the continent between Asia and the Atlantic Ocean.

ex · per · i · ment (eks per′ ə mənt) *n.* a test that is used to discover or prove something.

F

far (fär) *adv.* at or to a great distance *adj.* distant in time or space.

fear · less (fir′ lis) *adj.* feeling or showing no fear; not afraid; brave.

feath · er (feth′ ər) *n.* one of the light growths that cover a bird's skin.

France (frans) *n.* a country in western Europe.

free (frē) *adj.* having one's liberty; not under control of another. *adv.* without cost.

free · dom (frē′ dəm) *n.* the condition of being free; liberty.

friend · ly (frend′ lē) *adj.* **1.** like a friend; showing friendship. **2.** not angry or fighting, not hostile.

G

Gal · i · le · i, Gal · i · le · o (gal′ē lā′ē, gal′ə lē′ō) 1564–1642, Italian astronomer, physicist, and mathematician.

gas (gas) *n.* **1.** gasoline. Gasoline is a liquid that burns easily and that is used as a fuel for cars, airplanes, trucks, and boats. **2.** a form of matter that is not solid or liquid.

glide   (glīd) v. **glid·ed, glid·ing.** to move slowly along without any effort.

grand·fa·ther   (grand' fä' thər) n. the father of one's mother or father.

grav·i·ty   (grav' ə tē) n., pl. **grav·i·ties.** the force that pulls things toward the center of the earth.

han·dle   (hand' əl) n. the part of an object that is made to be grasped by the hands.

hear   (hir) v. **heard, hear·ing.** to receive sound through the ears.

heard   (hėrd) See **hear.**

heat   (hēt) v. to make or become hot or warm. n. The state of being hot; high temperature; warmth.

heav·y   (hev' ē) adj. having great weight; hard to lift or move.

help·ful   (help' fəl) adj. giving help; useful.

he·ro   (hir' ō) n., pl. **he·roes.** a person who is looked up to by others for having done something brave or outstanding.

high·way   (hī' wā') n. a main road.

hill   (hil) n. a raised, rounded part of the earth's surface.

hold   (hōld) v. to take and keep in the hands or arms; grasp; grip.

hope·less   (hōp' lis) adj. having or giving no hope.

In·di·an   (in' dē ən) n. a member of one of the tribes living in the Americas before Europeans arrived there.

Ja·pan   (jə pan') n. an island country in the North Pacific, off the eastern coast of Asia.

just   (just) adv. merely; only.

---

a b**a**t, ā c**a**ke, ä f**a**ther, är c**a**r, âr d**a**re; e h**e**n, ē m**e**, ėr t**e**rm; i b**i**b,
ī k**i**te, ir cl**ea**r; o t**o**p, ō r**o**pe, ô s**a**w, oi c**oi**n, ôr f**o**rk, ou **ou**t;
u s**u**n, u̇ b**oo**k, ü m**oo**n, ū c**u**te; ə **a**bout, tak**e**n

249

K

ki · lom · e · ter (ki lom′ ə tər *or* kil′ ə mē′ tər) *n.* a unit of length in the metric system, equal to 1,000 meters.

kit (kit) *n.* a set of parts or materials to be put together.

knew (nü *or* nū) See **know.**

know (nō) *v.* **knew, known, know · ing.** to understand clearly; be certain of the facts or truth of.

L

large (lärj) *adj.* big in size or amount.

late (lāt) *adj.* coming after the usual time.

law (lô) *n.* a rule made by a government for all the people in a town, state, or country.

lens (lenz) *n., pl.* **lens · es.** a piece of glass or other clear material that is curved to make light rays move apart or come together.

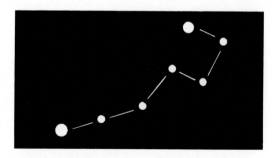

Lit · tle Dip · per (lit′ əl dip′ ər) a group of stars in the northern sky that are in the shape of a dipper, a cup with a handle. *See also,* **Big Dipper.**

Ly · on (lē ōn′) *n.* a city in east-central France.

M

man (man) *n., pl.* **men.** an adult male person.

Mars (märz) *n.* the seventh largest planet.

maze (māz) *n.* a confusing series of paths or passageways through which a person may have a hard time finding the way.

melt   (melt) *v.* to change from a solid to a liquid by heating.

men   (men) *See* **man.**

mile   (mīl) *n.* a unit of linear measurement equal to 5,280 feet.

Milk · y Way   (mil′ kē wā′) a cloudy white path that stretches across the sky at night, made up of thousands of stars.

mil · lion   (mil′ yən) *n.* one thousand times one thousand.

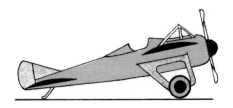

mod · el air · plane   (mod′ ēl ar′ plān′) a small-sized copy of an airplane.

moon   (mün) *n.* a heavenly body that revolves around the earth from west to east once every 29 1/2 days.

N

NASA   (nas′ ə) National Aeronautics and Space Administration.

New Jer · sey   (nü′ jėr′ zē or nū′ jėr′ zē) *n.* a state in the eastern United States.

North Car · o · li · na   (nôrth′ kär′ ə lī′ nə) *n.* a state in the southeastern United States.

O

oil   (oil) *n.* any one of a large group of substances that are greasy and will not dissolve in water.

once   (wuns) *adv.* in time past; before. *n.* one single time.

on · ly   (ōn′ lē) *adv.* exclusively; solely.

op · er · a · tor   (op′ ə rā′ tər) *n.* a person who operates, or works, a machine or other device.

O · sa · ka   (ō sä′ kə) *n.* a port city in southwestern Japan.

P

pack   (pak) *v.* to place in something for storing or carrying.

Par · is   (par′ is) *n.* the capital and largest city of France.

---

a b**a**t, ā c**a**ke, ä f**a**ther, är c**a**r, är d**a**re; e h**e**n, ē m**e**, ėr t**e**rm; i b**i**b,
ī k**i**te, ir cl**e**ar; o t**o**p, ō r**o**pe, ô s**a**w, oi c**o**in, ôr f**o**rk, ou **o**ut;
u s**u**n, ủ b**oo**k, ü m**oo**n, ū c**u**te; ə **a**bout, tak**e**n

pas · sen · ger (pas′ ən jər) *n.* a person who travels in an automobile, bus, train, airplane, or boat.

Penn · syl · va · nia (pen′ səl vān′ yə) *n.* a state in the eastern United States.

phone (fōn) *n.* a telephone; an instrument used to send sound over a distance. *v.* **phoned, phon · ing.** to call on the telephone.

pine (pīn) *n.* an evergreen tree that has cones and leaves that look like needles.

Po · lar · is (pō lar′ is) *n.* a star, also called the North Star, located in the northern sky above the North Pole.

pow · er (pou′ ər) *n.* the ability or right to do or cause something; strength or authority.

pre · vent (pri vent′) *v.* to keep something from happening.

print (print) *n.* a mark made by pressing into something.

Q

Queen E · liz · a · beth (kwēn′ i liz′ ə bəth) the queen of England from 1558 to 1603.

R

rail · road (rāl′ rōd′) *n.* all the tracks, stations, and cars that are part of a system of transportation by rail.

Ra · leigh, Sir Wal · ter (rô ′lē, sėr′ wôl′ tər) 1552?–1618, English adventurer and author.

reach (rēch) *v.* to arrive at; come to.

res · cue squad (res′ kū skwod′) a group of people who work together to save other people who are in danger.

rise (rīz) *v.* **rose, ris · en, ris · ing.** to move from a lower to a higher place; go upward.

Ro · a · noke Is · land (rō′ ə nōk′ ī′ lənd) *n.* an island off the coast of North Carolina where Sir Walter Raleigh attempted to start a colony.

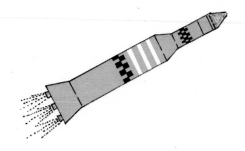

rock · et   (rok′ it) *n.* a device that is driven forward by a stream of hot gases that are released from the rear.

S

safe · ty   (sāf′ tē) *n.* freedom from harm or danger.

sail   (sāl) *v.* to move through the air or water, or travel over the water.

seat   (sēt) *n.* **1.** something to sit on. **2.** a place to sit.

seat belt   (sēt′ belt′) a strap or set of straps that may be buckled to hold a person in the seat of a car or airplane.

set   (set) *v.* **set, set · ting.** to go down.

set · tle   (set′ əl) *v.* **set · tled, set · tling.** to make a home in a place.

sev · en   (sev′ ən) *adj.* numbering one more than six.

shall   (shal) *v.* **1.** used to express future time. I *shall* show you my model airplane. **2.** used in questions when *shall* is expected in the answer. *Shall* we go? Yes, we *shall*.

shine   (shīn) *v.* **shone** *or* **shined, shin · ing.** to give forth light; be bright; glow.

Shin · kan · sen   (shin · kən · sen′) *n.* a railroad line for high-speed trains that opened between Tokyo and Osaka in 1964.

ship   (ship) *n.* **1.** a large boat. **2.** an airplane or spacecraft.

a bat, ā cake, ä father, är car, âr dare; e hen, ē me, ėr term; i bib, ī kite, ir clear; o top, ō rope, ô saw, oi coin, ôr fork, ou out; u sun, ů book, ü moon, ū cute; ə about, taken

shore (shôr) *n.* **1.** the land along the edge of an ocean, lake, or large river. **2.** land.

size (sīz) *n.* the amount of space something takes up; the length, width, and height of something.

slave (slāv) *n.* a person who is owned by another person.

slav · er · y (slā′ vər ē) *n.* the condition of being a slave.

so · lar (sō′ lər) *adj.* having to do with or coming from the sun.

soar (sôr) *v.* to fly high in the air.

SOS (es′ ō′ es′) a radio signal of distress.

sound (sound) *n.* what can be heard; noise.

south (south) *n.* the direction to your left as you watch the sun set in the evening.

space shut · tle (spās′ shut′ əl) *n.* a reuseable rocket-launched vehicle designed to go into earth orbit, to shuttle people and cargo to and from an orbiting spacecraft.

spark (spärk) *n.* a small bit of burning material.

speed (spēd) *n.* **1.** the rate of motion. **2.** quick or fast motion; swiftness. *v.* **sped** *or* **speed · ed, speed · ing.** to move quickly or rapidly.

start (stärt) *v.* to set out or make a beginning on something.

stay (stā) *v.* **1.** to wait in one place; not leave; remain. **2.** to keep on being; continue.

strand (strand) *v.* to leave in a helpless position.

sud · den · ly (sud′ ən lē) *adv.* without warning; unexpectedly.

sup · ply (sə plī′) *v.* **sup · plied, sup · ply · ing.** to provide with something needed or wanted. *n., pl.* **sup · plies.** a quantity of something that is needed or ready for use.

sur · prise (sər prīz′) *n.* **1.** a feeling of wonder and amazement caused by something unexpected. **2.** something that causes surprise.

T

tel · e · scope (tel′ ə skōp′) *n.* an instrument that makes distant objects seem larger and nearer.

tem · per · a · ture (tem' pər ə chər) *n.* the degree of heat or cold. A special instrument can measure the *temperature* of the air or of your body.

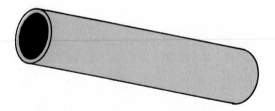

te · pee (tē' pē') *n.* a cone-shaped tent that is made of animal skins stretched over poles.

TGV (tē' gē' vē') short for *train à grande vitesse*, which is French for "high-speed train."

they'd (<u>th</u>ād) they would.

To · ky · o (tō' kē ō') *n.* the capital and largest city of Japan.

toll · booth (tōl' büth') *n.* a booth at a tollgate, where a toll is collected.

traf · fic (traf' ik) *n.* automobiles, airplanes, ships, or people moving along a route.

tube (tüb *or* tūb) *n.* a hollow piece of glass, rubber, plastic, metal or other material in the shape of a long pipe.

U

use · ful (ūs' fəl) *adj.* serving a good use or purpose; helpful.

V

ve · loc · i · pi · tis (və los' ə pī' tis) *n.* an imaginary disease or condition.

Vir · gin · ia (vėr jin' yə) *n.* a state in the eastern United States.

W

warn (wôrn) *v.* to give advice or notice to.

---

a b**a**t, ā c**a**k**e**, ä f**a**th**er**, är c**a**r, âr d**a**re; e h**e**n, ē m**e**, ėr t**er**m; i b**i**b, ī k**i**t**e**, ir cl**ear**; o t**o**p, ō r**o**pe, ô s**a**w, oi c**oi**n, ôr f**o**rk, ou **ou**t; u s**u**n, u̇ b**oo**k, ü m**oo**n, ū c**u**te; ə **a**bout, tak**e**n

wave   (wāv) *n.* anything like the curving or rippling movement on the surface of the ocean or other body of water.

wax   (waks) *n., pl.* **wax · es.** any of various fatty substances that come from plants or animals.

we'd   (wēd) we had.

we'll   (wēl) **1.** we shall. **2.** we will.

west   (west) *n.* the direction you face when watching the sun set. *adj.* **1.** toward or in the west. **2.** coming from the west.

white   (hwīt) *adj.* having the lightest of all colors; having the color of fresh snow; opposite of black.

White, John   (hwīt′, jon′) the leader of a group sent by Sir Walter Raleigh to settle on Roanoke Island. White made a trip back to England and when he returned to America he found that the colonists had disappeared.

whose   (hüz) *pron.* The possessive case of who and which.

worst   (wėrst) *adj.* most bad.

would   (wu̇d) *v.* **1.** used to express future time. The ship *would* sail soon. **2.** used to express intention or determination.

wrong   (rông) *adj.* **1.** not correct or true. **2.** bad. *adv.* in a way that is not right; incorrectly.

X-1   (eks wun) *n.* a rocket airplane. Chuck Yeager flew faster than the speed of sound in the *X-1.*

Y

Yer · kes Ob · serv · a · to · ry   (yėr′ kēz əb zėr′ və tôr′ ē) *n.* a building in Williams Bay, Wisconsin, furnished with telescopes and other equipment for observing and studying the moon, planets, and stars.

you'd   (ūd) **1.** you had. **2.** you would.